THE BLIND OPTOMETRIST

Nancy Glassman, OD

THE BLIND OPTOMETRIST

Nancy Glassman, OD

ABETTERU PRODUCTIONS LTD.

NEW YORK, NY

Published in the United States
Abetteru Productions Ltd.
New York, NY

Library of Congress Cataloging-in-Publication Data
The Blind Optometrist/Glassman, Nancy
2016912037

ISBN 978-0-9974839-3-2 (hardback)
ISBN 978-0-9974839-0-1 (paperback)
ISBN 978-0-9974839-6-3 (eBook)
ISBN 978-0-9974839-9-4 (audible)

Book Designer: Robert L. Lascaro
Photographer: Joseph Frazz

Printed in the United States of America

Dedicated to

S & L

CONTENTS

· · · · · · · · ·

CONTENTS

· · · · · · · · ·

CONTENTS

. . . .

1
....

ORANGE JUICE

"THIS IS *IT*— THIS IS *IT*— I SMELL *IT*."

I awoke to my dad's voice shouting like twisted branches in a horror movie, only the music wasn't playing. What time was it? I raced out of bed—fuck—low blood pressure hit me as I caved to the floor. I stayed low for a moment. Willing myself up through the vertigo, I crouched into the hallway, peripherally glimpsing the musician—my sister Leslie, who was motioning to my cat T down the hallway.

But T already knew. She was sliding along the wall into my room— leading not following. T felt the fear before any of us—the way she moved—no games, head down. Even if she shared breakfast with my dad, the genome jungle guided her instinctually when she heard a primal scream. No soggy Cheerios for her to slurp up this morning. Leslie was eyeing me with jaws clenched, wearing boxers and an undershirt... wide awake from playing piano at 4:00 in the morning.

"Nan, we have to call Perlstein right now."

I nodded and she gently crept down the hall to the phone.

Leaping into their bedroom, I first noticed my mother—frozen. In her sleeveless lacy nightgown (with the sexiest clavicle) she was standing by the door, far away from the man she never slept apart from. Her hand was in her mouth (all fingers at once) chewing her nails off.

Then I saw him.

His eyes were closed, his chin straining upwardly as if someone were pulling it with a rope. He was shouting to no one. Had I slept through some of it?

I instantly knew what he meant by 'IT.'

Death. He smelled death and feared he was about to die.

He was hallucinating in a dream state. I didn't know if he was awake or asleep. He had tons of energy, but his body was stiff as rigor mortis. Like when you're dreaming and someone is chasing you, and you can't...move. You're frozen.

I had to act fast. He was traveling to a place I didn't want him to go. I got into the craziest head and responded:

"I know. I had it too. It was in the orange juice."

I said this calmly — no big deal — we all had smelled *The Smell.*

Would this work? What the hell was I saying? My mother started talking but stopped mid-sentence when he interrupted her:

"Nancy is the only one who understands," he said in a tightly stretched voice.

She watched as her lunatic husband and I continued our psychotic dialog. When I looked at my mother — I knew I was on my own.

"If it was in the orange juice, then how come you're okay?" he inquired.

Game on. He would make it if I could just outsmart him. If he'd let me.

"Well, it took about four hours to wear off. We were all sick, but we forgot to tell you."

"If I'm about to die, then how can you hear me?"

"Well, you're shouting so loudly. So that means you're *not* going to die… but yeah, that smell is the *worst.*"

On I went twisting his mind puzzles back at him. Then Perlstein arrived. Mid-run up the steps, he smiled down at me collapsed in the living room:

"Hi Nan, how ya doing?"

Seeing him at that hour was so weird. Even if I told him the most intimate things in my life, he didn't belong *in* it. Why was he dressed so normally with his typical open blazer as if he were going to work at this hour? How was he here? The person I admired most came over to save my dad?

He was our hero — unshakable. He had a smile even in the direst circumstances. He'd been in WWII, so this wasn't a big deal — just another patient losing his mind. He'd fix it.

He had piercing eyes without any twist behind them — dealing straight, every time. He walked with a hurried gait, sometimes skipping a few steps at once, whistling, his head lurching forward. Probably some scoliosis, but it gave him an air of importance, as if he were leaning in to save the next disaster. He wanted to get there sooner.

"How's school going, Nan?"

I shot him a strange look. How can we act like this is normal?

He walked down the hall into the bedroom, easily finding his way in a home he'd never been:

3

"Hey Lenny, what's happening?"

"Oh, hello Dr. Perlstein"—said in a perfectly eloquent voice even though he'd just been screaming at the top of his lungs (while his eyes stayed shut). Perlstein stayed two hours.

My father was on the verge of a seizure. Perlstein said my dialog prevented it by calming him down. We had a clue a few weeks prior. During local trips with my mom, he'd swiftly dart out of the car and run. Leslie would try to find him during these running rampages.

The culprit? The cause of his 'flight syndrome'? Benadryl. When you suddenly withdraw from it, if you've been taking it a couple of months and you're in your 60s, a nice little paranoia will set in. And if you're already nuts…get ready to be admitted. He wound up in the hospital for five days in withdrawal.

My father was a sad man. It reminded me of the night Leslie and I were coming home from the city. It was long after midnight, driving on Rockaway Turnpike.

"Did you see that man?" I shouted.

"What man?"

"That old man in the middle of the road. Standing there on the island… Go back!"

"At this hour?"

"He could get killed!"

Les turned the car around and we drove back, looking for him. After a mile she started getting pissed. Then, "Oh my God, you're right…there he is."

A man in his 80s was standing in the middle of a narrow island, with cars zooming past at 70 mph in each direction. We carefully pulled over and after a break in the line of speeding cars I ran up to him, asking his name. I was relieved he knew it. Milton was lost.

"Can you help me?" he asked in the kindest voice, as his stylish windbreaker flapped in the wake of the Turnpike traffic.

He wasn't nervous, just confused. Probably like my grandmother when friends she had made that day broke her finger to take her favorite and only ring. She didn't know her emerald was worth a few thousand.

We stayed with our new friend until the cops arrived. I didn't trust cops though, a residual effect of being engaged to the child of Holocaust survivors. They took him to some senior center they discovered he belonged to.

Milton.

Why did I like him so much? He seemed nicer than my dad, but still— I equated my father with Milton. Someone who couldn't be safe. What island would he wind up on? I feared who would come to his rescue.

My father's slide started with 'cycling.' I'm still not sure what that means. I only know how he acted. He would have two weeks of elation, followed by two weeks of depression. These cycles would repeat, until he would have shorter durations of each phase. There was no middle road. Supposedly this happens when a certain psychotropic med has been taken for a while in susceptible individuals. Particularly if the med has been removed and retried a few times.

The person understands what is happening only during the depression phase, if they're lucky. When they're manic they don't want to understand anything—it's so much fun. When they get depressed again, it's deeper. When the mania returns it's worse because they're petrified of the oncoming depression, so they become frantic trying to keep the 'high' going.

Some people just have the mania. They never come down, except when they go to jail or hide away in their third home. The one your worthless stock investment paid for. These unipolar manics return again and again with those buff bods and rehabilitated values. They prosper even in jail. They may feel a little low, but they'll never feel *your* low.

Unipolar manics are charming, until you realize they're sick. "I'm so successful, so what's the problem?" A little sociopathy never hurt anyone.

The unipolar MD I know blamed his second failed marriage on his much younger beautiful wife's bipolar. They got divorced because *she* wouldn't take her meds.

Perlstein took my father off the Nardil, to try another med before he retired. "I don't want to leave him half a man." Perlstein had a mission to cure my dad.

He said most shrinks don't understand MAOIs so they don't prescribe them. It has dietary restrictions that scare shrinks about liability. Yet it has zero sexual side effects for women. Instead shrinks prefer to prescribe SSRIs, which can ruin a woman's libido.

If she got depressed about that, they could always up the meds and bill more hours. ●●

2

....

GET DOWN

My father had Post-Traumatic Stress Disorder from a mugging, years earlier. It was timed right before closing.

The crackhead pushed through the front door when my dad was locking his office. He held the gun to my father's head and made him tie the secretary and optician's wrists with wire and put them in an exam room. Then he dragged my dad through the office, gun to his head, threatening to kill him if he made one wrong move. Somehow he *knew* my father kept cash in a safe. My dad stayed cool and distracted the gunman.

The optician was then untied and instructed to tie up my father. The optician didn't have a wallet, watch, or cent on him and seemed too calm to the police who took the report afterward. An *inside job* they speculated, especially since it was my father's 50th birthday. The cops sensed the gunman knew the new optician — 'Choo-Choo.'

Years later, at a salon in The Village, the Latin woman washing my hair wore wild frames. When I inquired, she told me her dad was an optician soon to retire in Brooklyn. My unconscious added the years as my brain clamped down. Before I could switch topics she said: "They call him Choo-Choo."

Some people never have to return to the scene. Others suffer continual grief from working or residing where the incident took place. My father had to go back to a place he always loved. He had a responsibility to us. He was in charge in his office, in his home, in his life. No more.

My father didn't have the luxury of knowing his mugger's identity, or that he was behind bars. They never caught him.

My father came home to another shock in a few days — a surprise party my mother had planned for months. My dad's reaction to the mugging hadn't begun yet. I inherited this tendency of a delayed inner response. If you're the quiet type like my dad, no one expects you to react. When you *finally* react, no one realizes because it's so long after the impact. The odd behaviors you unexpectedly display are from a trauma months ago.

Weaker souls become vengeful. Some of them are the friends who make you feel like crap when you get off the phone with them. Angry, bitter, always a jab. When asked how to diffuse anger, an Australian Rabbi said:

"Ask yourself what made them that way."

My father finally reacted months later when my mother was diagnosed with MS. My mother handled her diagnosis with guts. He didn't get angry. He fell apart.

I dropped out of college for two years. I had a presentation in one of my classes. I couldn't do it. Instead of telling my MIS professor about my fear of public speaking, I had a breakdown. I had a 3.92 cumulative GPA.

Leslie had warned: "Remember Nan — you can never study too much." My sister who never studied at all, told me:

"Make sure there's never a question you won't know the answer to."

She loved manipulating me and it always worked. The only two Bs I ever got were in English, my favorite class. So I avoided taking English. I didn't choose any easy major though. MIS was considered the hardest major in the school—but that could never be true. Nothing was harder than analyzing Shakespeare and pleasing a professor who couldn't get over Ronald Reagan being elected President:

"An actor — Oh my God," she kept repeating.

I decided to fail an MIS exam and give myself a reason to drop out. It was the first time in my life I didn't study. When I got my grade back I looked in disbelief at the 'A.'

Somehow I managed to lose enough weight that my family got nervous and stopped bugging me to stay in school.

The only symptom I had was 'critical self-awareness,' an awful and *silent* unremitting repetition of every single goddamn thing I said. It was like a skipped tape recorder. Anything I said would repeat silently and immediately right after I said it, like a double connection on your cell.

That echo. echo echo echo echo

It made it impossible to have a conversation.

I guess that's what happens when some catastrophic fear sets in, without any source. There's no earthquake, no fire, no attack. That's what's so frightening. When you're afraid for no reason there's no way to manage it.

Before I dropped out, my MIS professor handed me a recommendation he wrote. He wasn't supposed to show it to me because elite investment banks were paranoid that students could alter their professor's recommendations. Potential employers would request that the documents be sealed. But this nice man wanted to share his masterpiece. He didn't know he would give me 10 minutes of my life back.

As he read it to me the weight lifted. I was me again. His praise was unexpected. Was I this person he was speaking of? The depression I couldn't get a handle on vanquished spontaneously. For almost 10 entire minutes I walked on campus as if everything were fine. Not only fine, euphoric. Anything above severe depression is an enormous relief. I had the objectivity to realize during this brief reprieve that my ego must be severely damaged, because why else would this nerd's accolades make me human again. Before I knew it, my mood descended with a weight I couldn't shake. And back I was in hell.

He gave me a copy of his grandiose image, so I read it like some pill. The fix lasted for a shorter duration, only two minutes. After that, it lost its effect. I was nothing again. What happened to make me feel this way? What caused this shift in my chemistry? Only one thing in my life had changed. And I didn't feel *that* was the reason.

I told Dr. Perlstein that my mom's MS wasn't why I had to immediately leave school. It was the oral report. He said I would know.

Years later he said the *onset* of my mom's MS caused my entire family to destabilize. I always wondered why I simply didn't ask my adoring professor to give me another assignment. Urgency replaced my perspective as if I had no choice. Dropping out of college didn't bring the relief I sought. I became ridden with shame.

I remember one day feeling especially vulnerable. I was going to see Perlstein. If Perlstein had said one mean, undercutting, nasty thing, it would have destroyed me. The psychiatrist wields more power over any patient in medicine.

Power over your mind.

Patients can't defend themselves and their treatment is behind closed doors. You're on your own. The psychiatrist knows this. Perlstein protected me during the worst time in my life.

If I had dropped out for nothing other than avoiding my oral report, I soon had a reason. In a few weeks my mother suffered her worst MS attack.

It was a blood-curdling scream: *"LENNYYYY!"* And then a thump.

My father airlifted off the bed and landed with one foot on the ground, loping into the bathroom, and catching her out of the air before she hit the ground. The house shook. The thump was his foot landing, instead of her frame.

She couldn't move for three weeks. Usually you have vertigo in certain positions, but she had it in all positions except one. I slept on the floor by their bed and my sisters took different shifts trying to feed her. My sister Deanna, who never changed the sheets on her own bed, changed her bedpans. Leslie serenaded her with *Pennies from Heaven* and other tunes she loved.

As I watched my mother tilt on her left side in agony, a thought occurred to me.

I'd never have a child — not with this genome.

The thought was like a blinker flashing on and off. It was bad enough they might inherit my dislocated shoulders, but I wouldn't want MS to do the skip-a-generation thing and get them. I knew it wasn't supposed to be heritable but that could change. Anything can mutate. Science constantly changes what they thought they knew.

My mom managed to eat small bits of fruit but lost 25 pounds. She wanted to die. As soon as she recovered, she confessed another two weeks would have been too hard. My father caved and we became that dysfunctional family down the block.

We managed 13 more years with him on a roller coaster. Perlstein became central.

My mother had 'benign' MS and never suffered anything as severe as that attack. Every year when the seasons would change she would have a smaller attack, take meclizine and recover in weeks. She couldn't take any of the common MS drugs, as they would cause an MS attack.

No one knew why. It's possible she was allergic to an additive in the med.

The rheumatologist said her pain wasn't from her arthritis. The neurologist said her pain wasn't from her MS. We learned to ignore them.

Although she had chronic pain in her feet, she accepted it and never spoke about it. She got rid of all the MS supporters who told her how bad it would get. She threw out the scooter salesperson. She read everything she could and spoke about it in a clinical way. She distanced her Self from this inconvenience.

She coped. My father did not. 👓

3

....

BLACKJACK

My father developed a Blackjack craze. It replaced the rush of racquetball because Nardil, his antidepressant, made it hard to balance in the court. Nardil also gave him painful erections, and their once incredible sex life came to an abrupt halt. Blackjack replaced all this.

Every weekend he dragged my mother to Atlantic City. They became *Regulars*. Stretch limos picked them up and decadent meals and rooms were 'comp'd.' He played until 6:00 a.m., leaving her alone except for short meals — then rushing back to the table. She stayed in the room reading a book. She said there was zero prejudice in Atlantic City, because the casinos wanted your money. That was the nice part.

She ventured to his table one evening. She watched a familiar stranger shout:

"DO IT, DO IT, *DO IT!*"

He had a system — card counting. He said it was legal as long as no one knew. His friends would lose large sums, but Lenny would walk if he lost more than $500. He often won, and happily grew a larger and larger stash in his closet.

He made new friends and soon had a group of men for his day-only trips. He was so popular that they wanted to hang out with him even when they weren't gambling. How did my father make friends wherever he went?

My dad's pals were terrific guys — dry humored, standup, and loving the camaraderie. My mother was often alone. Somehow they didn't grow apart emotionally.

This is what shrinks have a hard time with. Couples whose love surpasses any rational equation. No one would put up with it, unless they had *that* kind of love.

I'm still confused about what a healthy love is. Is it better to have a healthy love and leave a person if they become dysfunctional, because staying means you're co-dependent? When does your own life take precedence over the welfare of the one you love? Why does it become 'your' life and not 'our life,' just because one of you gets sick? And when couples *did* part because they didn't have the kind of love my parents had, did that mean they were healthier?

I asked Perlstein: "How do people go home every night to the same person if they don't feel that passion? If they're just needy?"

"Very easily," he replied.

I asked Leslie: "Would you rather have a peaceful relationship with someone and no passion, or that passionate love where they were always driving you crazy?"

"The passionate love of course — what are you kidding?" ●–●

4

....

THE EXPERTS

I'd like to stop cursing, but driving ruins that. I never use the word 'shit' and I can't stand when others do. I can say 'fuck' 10 times a day—but no, not 'shit.'

My father almost died because of shit. It was the initial reason we thought he was going insane.

My father never missed a single day of work, except twice when he was snowed in. Perlstein kept him together from 1982 to 1995. But right before Perlstein retired he took my father off the Nardil. And for the first time in over 20 years, my father missed work. January 10th and January 17th of 1995.

He was walking around grabbing his ass, saying it was killing him.

For two entire weeks he would not shut up. He was so nutty my mom called me. Then I spoke with Perlstein who said: "What choice do you have?"

No one knew my father was undergoing a rebound reaction from discontinuing Nardil.

I was in grad school and needed help with this decision. Leslie said don't call 911. Even if she was stoned she knew. But Leslie wasn't helping, she was snorting. So I called the ambulance, trusting Perlstein would be there. I didn't know he would retire right in the middle of the crisis.

My father's mental state was high functioning prior to his incarceration. He wrote an incredibly coherent letter before his hospitalization, explaining his symptoms to Perlstein. He also fixed the air conditioner in their bedroom. He bought a motor and installed it himself.

My father was hospitalized from February 7th to March 4th, for what was thought to be a post-traumatic stress reaction to Perlstein's retirement. Before Perlstein left, he tried Zoloft. My father got a full body rash.

My father was in the hands of Dr. K. for the next three weeks. Dr. K. said my father's physical pain was psychological. It was because Perlstein left. All the psychiatrists concurred.

They reached their unanimous decision without a physical exam, not even a cursory rectal exam or colonoscopy were performed to rule out my father's chief complaint:

SEVERE RECTAL PAIN

They gave him a stool hardener; not realizing the diarrhea was a mock symptom. As the impaction grew so did the diarrhea because the new feces had nowhere to go, except leak around the enormous ball of shit blocking it.

Ignoring the patient's chief complaint was the way the rest of his treatment would play out as they proceeded to destroy his other end—his brain.

Psychiatry (unlike other fields) is private and hidden. There is no way to catch an incompetent shrink. Shrink errors are rarely accountable. They don't have cameras in mental hospitals to protect the patients from the whacko staff who mercilessly reinforce their powerlessness.

What kind of procedure code and which diagnosis do they decide you fit from research over 50 years ago or new research interpreted for the pharmaceutical industry? Research that is suddenly proven wrong after you've been told 'past is prologue' and now it's *future expectations* that predicts a successful outcome.

Dr. K tried Paxil, which caused Parkinson's syndrome—shakes, rigidity, and baby steps. My father would shuffle and stare into space. He kept falling. They didn't mind.

Instead of removing the Paxil, they added Prolixin, which caused urinary retention, along with tardive dyskinesia.

Next they took him off Synthroid to 'test him,' which caused more constipation. No one cared he never received a shower or a new pair of socks.

They locked him out of his room, forcing him to walk the hall all day holding up his pants, because they confiscated his belt. They also took his shoes. He shuffled along robbed of any semblance of dignity. He was forced to eat only with the group and denied any right to privacy. Every day was excruciating. They call this 'behavior modification.'

My dad was never a talker and the only group he liked was at the gym or the casino. He was a man's man—extremely popular yet quiet.

He was quiet at home too, except for his sudden outbursts. His voice was so deep, he seldom had to raise it. My father was possessive: *My* TV, *My* car, *My* room. To the outside world, he was a shy funny man everyone loved to be around, but he could do without.

"All I need is you," he would tell my mom.

He was a tremendous athlete, with great aim and formidable strength as a ball player. He would stand in the center of the court as men half his age sweated for the shots.

But finally the shrinks broke him. He gave in and accepted his fate. In spite of the fog he lived in, he knew his life lay in the hands of incompetent schlubs.

And this is what gave me the worst heartache — that he *knew* they were slowly destroying him.

The psychiatrists wanted to take all control away from this less than half a man. Until they 'treated him,' my father was still functioning. No one seemed to notice his advancing rigidity. They kept playing with his meds. But his benefits were running out so they terminated treatment.

Government still views mental illness as something you *choose* to have, as opposed to diabetes, cancer, and heart disease.

I never heard of a bipolar patient eating too much meat which caused thickening of their mood.

The liver transplant who keeps drinking and smoking will be treated with respect. They pay for *that* patient to get the best care. But the mental patient, who did nothing but get traumatized, or inherit chemical imbalance, is treated like garbage.

Upon returning home, within a 24-hour period, his left pupil became fixed and dilated. He couldn't make eye contact, nor perform simple eye movement tests. He couldn't move any part of his body. He lost control of his bladder and fell out of bed. The meds produced a rigid catatonia and an ambulance rushed him to the ER. He was now in the hospital for a physical condition, which is what it always had been.

The hospital. The antiseptic long halls with the silver, clanking medicine trays. The gray floors being mopped by some former inmate lucky to have a job, who may linger around your loved one at night. The artwork of miserable faces lining the walls, greeting you while you instantly realize the morons who chose that art are incapable of helping your loved one. The overworked, cold nurses at their stations; the ones who want to kill you for asking for one of those tiny tissue boxes designed to drive you even crazier. The angel, whose smile contrasts with all the abuse and saves your sanity.

While he was in the local hospital, the attending physician decided to reduce his Xanax and eliminate the Paxil. This was done on a whim, without a reason. Reducing the Xanax created a severe withdrawal so that he suffered two-minute whole body tremors at half-hour intervals — *for the next 10 days.*

I watched him silently sweat through these tremors. The doctor did nothing to end this nightmare.

Meanwhile, his impaction was ever expanding. He still hadn't had a rectal exam. He still hadn't voided his bowels.

He was now on Prolixin, Cogentin, and not enough Xanax. Next they added Klonopin. My father complained about his stomach, so they gave him Librax. Now he was both constipated and couldn't pee. Perlstein and my mother warned the doctors if given certain drugs, my father would have urinary retention. No one listened.

They inserted a catheter, causing a huge infection. They gave him Bactrim for the infection. He developed an enormous rash.

By now he had an IV, catheter, and tremors every two to four minutes. They finally gave him Urecholine to urinate at my mother's insistence.

As soon as he got home from St. John's he passed out.

He went right back into Franklin for another three weeks, because we couldn't lift him and 911 gave us no choice.

During this last stay, the doctor threatened my mother — if my father did not submit to ECT, he would not treat him anymore.

My mother asked me what to do.

I watched a woman dress after she had ECT. She appeared slow and disoriented, like a little girl lost. It worked for Carrie Fisher, but she didn't have to remember how to diagnose glaucoma. Also the brain shrinks around 60 years old. Another doctor whispered not to do it. More worrisome was Franklin seemed to have financial troubles. I wondered what ECT generated in revenues. Ultimately, I made my decisions guided by what I thought my father would want.

He almost made it out of the hospital, but in the worn down, emasculated state he was in, he caught site of a woman and it blew the fuse. She appeared at the end of his stay. My mother saw her and knew it would be trouble as my father mumbled:

"She looks like my mother."

When he came home he succumbed to an infancy state, unable to brush his teeth. We took him to his primary:

"Lenny, you went to receive medical care, but they never examined you."

Dr. Beer had to stick his hand up my dad's ass and told me to leave the room.

"I'm not leaving."

Beer looked at me incredulously, and whispered something to my father.

My dad said: "She's staying!"

I held my father's hand as he screamed when Beer pulled a ton of hardened black rocks out of his ass. It wasn't over quickly. Beer could have given my father some kind of analgesic but pain is irrelevant.

After he removed three handfuls, he said it was a life-threatening impaction that required intestinal surgery.

We were on a mission. We bought Golytely. He sat in the kitchen drinking gallons of it and other liquids. Then we heard him painfully void part of the blockage.

On the third day, the pain was so bad we went to the ER again. And again I held his hand, while another doctor shoved his hand up my dad's ass.

My father was finally clear, except he had lost his brain.

If he wasn't lying in bed, he would have violent explosions. He took the TV and dropped it on the floor. He threw things. Yelled. I went through the house removing dangerous objects, worried if my mother was safe. He would walk into the kitchen and linger, not saying a word. Then he would shuffle back to his new rental bed—the kind that elevates like in the hospital.

Was my mom doomed to take care of her infant husband? Who *was* this man everyone had been so scared of? Her twice-a-day lover waking her in the midnight hours to make love. His huge underbite gave him a constant scowl, no matter how happy he was. I didn't understand her strength or how she had any left. What drove her?

Was it desperation? Compassion? Love?

She kept seeking—nothing would stand in her way, including her MS. She was getting the best doctor in town to reverse the damage. She kept thinking Perlstein was around the corner.

Every time we had another awful experience interviewing another shrink, she would find someone else also highly recommended—top of his field. At every appointment my mother recited the history of my father's illness, all the meds, all the reactions, until it was the end of the session and we were ushered out.

Perlstein told me there are two types of shrinks—the ones who want to learn about their own pathology to heal themselves, and the superman kind who *use* their patients to feel powerful.

It's no longer required that *shrinks get therapy* before graduating medical school. Perlstein said the first group make the better shrinks. He followed it with:

"It took a long time to whip this jackass into shape," about himself.

5

....

ROLE MODELS

Neither of my sisters was available. Deanna was finally enjoying a romantic marriage and no one wanted to burden her. Leslie was snorting cocaine every chance she got and no one wanted to be near her.

Dr. Perlstein had suggested Leslie take a walk in the park to cope with her devastation about our father.

"No one understands that I can't smile if my father is ill," she'd say.

Leslie would hang out with him every night trying to cheer him up, but it destroyed her.

She hadn't had sex in over 12 years, fearing AIDS and being the responsible person she was. She and I both need that one *special* person. Leslie met that special person in the park—an Italian mafioso wannabe hair stylist who carried a gun and a name to go with it.

Shaft got her started on coke again (she had a primer in college at 19). After a few weeks and some other drugs, Leslie was lost.

My best friend gone.

I never felt the need for friends because I already had the best in both my sisters. They were always there to rescue me and funnier than anyone else I knew. Leslie was the oldest by five years and Deanna was three years older than I was. They were extremely close before I came along, and they remained that way.

Deanna was my go-to until I turned 14. When I got to High School, I started hanging out with Les, as Deanna drifted away with guys.

Because I began developing in the third grade, when I reached 12 years old I could pass for legal at the casinos when traveling with my family. So when I hit 14, Leslie was 19 and we had no trouble getting into discos every night.

Dancing was the only time I got to be a person.

During the day I faded into the High School crowd. My friend George said men admired me from afar. Who knew? None of them spoke to me.

Some of my teachers noticed and it was hard covering up. I didn't want attention from 30-year-old unhappily married men. I'd walk on the street and only boys *not* in my school would make flattering comments. Anyone I did know never said a complimentary word. Discos saved me.

Eighties disco—*Donna Summer, Shalamar, Prince…*

I came home one night after 3:00 a.m. My father was standing at the top of the stairs and threw a shoe at me.

"Dad, please—it's the only happiness I know."

He looked at me for a second: "Okay," and shuffled back into his room. Secretly they were relieved I did something besides hide away studying.

My mother said: "I'd rather they have sex in the house, than worry where they are. Some kids hide things from their parents but you don't have to hide anything from me." She was talking about my sisters.

Only I wish she had said: "Nancy—don't feel pressure from your sisters—wait 'til it's a guy you admire."

My sisters had a hard time setting that example.

Leslie met a man she liked but when I walked by he came after me. I dumped him. This sort of favor was one my sisters never returned. Instead, they came on to men I had dated, which hurt deeply.

Deanna continuously made fun of my lack of experience, while her friend stood behind her saying: "If I had a younger sister, and she was prettier than me, she'd be dead."

Leslie, the 21-year-old who had sex at 19 and drank until she threw up; Deanna, the 19-year-old who had sex at 13 and never drank. My sisters were polar opposites, both to each other and within themselves. I was 16 and under their influence. Maybe it wasn't the best thing. But I trusted them and there was no one else I ever would.

Now, both my sisters were emotionally out of my life.

The most painful part was Leslie. My big sister. Leslie had always kept me going. She dragged me to hear jazz and other music whenever I had a free weekend. I'd watch her dance alone at a club without any inhibition. She was so smooth.

An accomplished jazz pianist, who was so opinionated I became obnoxious quoting her. *Bill Evans sucked, Coltrane was annoying, and don't talk about Miles.*

The only musicians she respected were Bird, Prez, and Lady. (And of course Beethoven, Mozart, and Bach.)

She said Stevie Wonder was a genius, then later blamed him for ruining music with the electric keyboard. She blamed Elvis for something else. Faddis couldn't be that bad if Dizzy let him take the high notes, and Prince did things no one else had done before. Leslie was impossible.

Sal Mosca was her maestro and substitute father. A man who ate nuts with a spoon out of respect for his piano; so he wouldn't get oil on it. Sal commanded a small cult-like group of followers whose only problem was him. They were purists and rejected every form of commercial music, except Barbra Streisand. Sal loved Barbra.

It was a relief to be around people immune to untalented fame seekers. But it was a huge sacrifice for Leslie. No longer would she ski, as she could injure her thumbs. She stopped playing gigs because they weren't respecting her music. She forgot about searching for an apartment because she wouldn't be able to play till 6:00 a.m. But this was okay.

Her aspirations were to please only Sal, who encouraged her isolation from the rest of the world.

Sal and Shaft.

Leslie only involved herself with men who tried to dominate her but she would never commit to them.

It was doomed from the start and the only kind of love she wanted.

6

....

A MIRACLE

I felt so lost that I took off a Saturday from work to go to a retreat. My friend Lewis was running a workshop on miracles and decided to make me his afternoon project. This was a miracle in itself.

The informal group of therapists, healers, and seekers like me sat outside the upstate home of a High Priestess. They made a circle around me, as I sat on a chair trying not to look self-conscious. Lewis called in the spirits asking them for guidance and to find me a date.

They put such energy into it. One man was dripping with sweat and singing. Another woman raised my arms to the sky: "Please bless Nancy with fertility."

They danced, sang, smoked, and played the drums.

The sweaty man shouted: "Nancy—let your hair down!"

Another woman came over ecstatically: "He likes to fish, and *you know him already*."

The drummer gazed straight ahead—one cool guy, with eyes that had been through hell. His partner had buckteeth and chunks of fat hanging off her frame. She slowly rose from beside him, a glow upon her face, as her body moved to his beat. Her buckteeth smiled and she became radiant. He depended on her dearly to keep him safe from his demons. He looked only at her. Maybe I could find a man like that.

Lewis took his time strolling deliberately toward me—he had waited for everyone else to give me their message. I looked up at him eagerly to hear what his serious face implied.

"What I heard from the spirits is that you have to interview 101 men and not get attached to any of them until you're done. You have to go into bars and restaurants and hotels, and other public places and you have to promise to do this." *Pressure on.*

I created a survey to hide behind:

1. What was your longest relationship and when did it end?

2. What kinds of music do you like?

3. Is traveling important to you? What if the woman didn't want to?

4. Do you like animals?

5. Do you want someone with the same religion or cultural background?

6. Is fine dining a real value to you?

7. Do you consider yourself a monogamous person or do you enjoy frivolous sex?

8. How would you describe your parents' relationship?

9. Who do you admire?

I got right on it and even bought a little brown book to record the responses. I was reaching out to everyone with this ridiculous interview work, rolling with momentum and forcing my shyness away. It was easy picking up men on the street once I engaged them.

I approached and interviewed 16 men. Only one guy sitting on a bench said no. He was sharing an intimate moment with his dog. I had to respect that.

Talking to strangers got me to start networking in my business too. I called so many people that I forgot I had called Bram with a question about my building.

The following Tuesday morning, Morda, my secretary, yanked me out of an exam. I thought something really bad happened. She dragged me down the hallway jumping up and down and raising my hands up to the ceiling: *"IT'S BRAM! IT'S BRAM!"*

I got on the phone after adjusting my head. We both kept saying "Hi," over and over.

Could it really be him?

"So, you're a doctor?"

"Well, kind of."

He quickly moved from talking about family (both of us had devastating news) to marriage:

"So, ya married?"

"I never got married. You got married, right?"

"Divorced. Ya wanna go out?"

"Okay."

"How 'bout tonight?"

"Okay." It never occurred to me he was divorced.

"Here's my cell…and I might as well give you my home…and I guess you already have my office number," he laughed.

I pictured his hair. It wasn't running amok anymore, but parted on the side and cut short to match his CEO status. He wore a white, buttoned down shirt with his slim, strong arms glistening in his rolled up sleeves, sitting behind an enormous desk, running his huge company.

What if I had never broken up with him?

When I was 25 I thought of calling him, but Leslie continued to discourage me, saying he'd have slimy cum. I nodded. But how'd she know?

I met him at summer camp when I turned 12. He wasn't yet 15, but three years made him incredibly older.

What was it? His soft voice, calm facade, or the way he locked into my eyes?

Deanna introduced us. They looked like twins — same hair, same skin tone, even their freckles matched.

The day he lost his virginity wasn't noticed by anyone but me. I don't know how I knew, but when you're keenly attuned to someone, things are obvious even when you're 12. The memory is still vivid: he was leading an older woman away.

She kept turning her face toward me nervously: "What are you looking at?" she asked.

The jailbait smiled and dragged her off. A very unattractive cello player.

When I came back for the rest of the summer, after a trip home, he jumped to bring my bags down. Chewing on a pencil, he threw it out of his mouth when he saw me:

"I thought you left!"

I gleamed over the fact that he thought of me at all.

I'd catch glimpses of him over the years. Smiles and brief hellos as we both began to take longer looks. I was always too young. My breasts weren't though, and I knew he heard all the jokes about me at camp. They even fell out of my bathing suit once, when I was water skiing. My shoulder dislocated and I was climbing into the boat. One of the kids said:

"Can you pull your top down a little lower?"

My shoulder hurt so much but I managed to get them inside.

Bram wouldn't stare at them though, not the way the others would. Maybe this protected me from a too early sexual encounter with my only love. He had already slept with so many girls—I'm grateful I wasn't one of them.

He was my dream—and momentary reprieve from painful loneliness. He saw me for who I was, even if I felt completely lost. He had a rare sensitivity for someone so young.

When I turned 17, Deanna told me to call him. His dad answered and I bravely left my number. Bram called back the same night after 11:00 p.m. *(Was he back from fooling around?)*

"My dad told me to call you up. He said you sound like a *W.A.W.*"

"A what?"

"A *wild-ass-woman*. So what do you look like now?"

"I'd shock you."

"How 'bout shocking me tonight?"

"Okay."

"What's your address? I'll be there in half an hour."

I was going out with Bram—Yippee!

When he arrived, he didn't have a chance. For the first time in my life, *he* was shy. He could not stop smiling and glancing my way. He was at my mercy.

We had a few dates, and it happened—oral sex.

I was so nervous; I couldn't relax. I was petrified I didn't look normal and there was Bram—the expert. Even in the dark, he seemed to know exactly where to go—which scared me even more. He'd done the operation a thousand times before. I pretended it wasn't my first time. He spent such a long time, I felt bad for him.

But he kept going, saying: "Practice makes perfect."

He told me not to worry, that we had all the time in the world. Still, I couldn't have an orgasm. I didn't know what it was. He had no trouble with my blowjob, even though I didn't know what I was doing.

Afterward, he hugged me for the rest of our date and made me feel something I hadn't in the longest time. *Acceptance.*

I had a nightmare a couple of nights after our first time together:

Bram was in the throes of ecstasy, cumming all over my ceiling like an enormous hose…out of control. I asked Dr. Perlstein about this years later.

He said: "Something about Bram frightened you."

After more dates and more blowjobs, Bram asked me to move to Santa Barbara.

He looked into my eyes: "It's a rough world out there Nancy. We should stick together."

He was switching schools and I was going away for my first year of college.

"Where would we live?" I asked, not believing I was having this conversation.

He said: "We could get a little house."

I pictured a beautiful home with a red tiled roof. I'd get pregnant, we'd get married, and we'd be divorced when he cheated on me. Bram was in demand—getting the nicest *practice* with his younger sister's friends. I wasn't even a person yet. I was still a virgin and every date scared me.

There was a much bigger thorn though: I was no longer infatuated with him. Leslie ruined it. She said: "Uchss" when he dropped me off one night.

Not even "ick" or "yuck"—but *"uchss."*

That did it. I was over my crush. Bram was nothing. An entire childhood of hero worship wiped out with one word that wasn't even a word. Leslie thought Bram was the pits. I didn't view him the same way ever again. It finished our romance.

Bram never knew why, although he also never confided something important to me: Leslie had given him a handjob at camp. She was embarrassed I was dating him. It was the real reason she sabotaged our relationship.

I found this out 26 years later.

I wanted to love him. He had it for me and I knew it. I just didn't feel it anymore. I didn't understand how my feelings could change so quickly for someone who meant so much to me.

I saw Bram again when he took me to a Springsteen concert, along with his sister and some guy no one can remember. I was home from my first year of college on a break. I had no clothes to fit the new pudgy me, and feared how bad I looked. He didn't notice. Not even when we stood on the chairs like everyone else at the Garden. I didn't want to stand on my chair but the entire audience was in cult worship of this God, a god I only used for masturbation purposes.

After the concert we went back to his house and he returned a necklace I'd left from the summer. He held on to it, not wanting to give it back, knowing he might not see me again.

All he said when he dropped me off was: "We never got a chance to make love."

I got out of the car as fast as I could. I had a feeling he liked to say "make love" even if he was having a one-night stand.

He called one last time at school: "I love the sound of your voice." I didn't want to hurt him, but I was distant.

"Do you want me to stop calling you?"

I said: "Maybe."

He said: "Take it easy."

Yet there was one more time — a vague time. It was the following summer. I was at a party with Leslie and had some wine. I had lost weight. I called Bram.

He flew over and when he entered the party it looked like a blazing fireball dropped from the sky. He was lit up and glowing from too much sun. He looked at me shyly, with his head down.

We made no attempt to hang out with the party but quickly found a room, after he grabbed a beer. We sat on the edge of the bed looking at each other. I was trying to feel it again.

"I must be in your unconscious because you call me when you have a drink."

I sat silent, suddenly shy.

"I was in bed and there was *no way* I was getting up, and then you called. You're the only person I would get out of bed for."

His hair was still wet.

"Nancy, I've been seeing someone this summer. She means nothing to me if—(his voice got quiet)—if you would be my girlfriend. But I know you don't want to move to Santa Barbara. Maybe you should drink more."

He carefully accentuated every word.

We kissed.

He was waiting, knowing, sad. I could never fake it with Bram.

I can't remember how we parted or even caring if he was upset. I only felt down.

I didn't get the feeling.

Now, he had called me back. After 26 years. He called my apartment later that night:

"I can't believe I'm calling you at home."

Then I knew. I could hear it in his voice. He still felt it.

My mother said: "Of course he'll remember you."

But I couldn't trust her opinion, she thought too highly of me.

I asked: "Am I late?" still paranoid from my last boyfriend's constant criticism.

After many seconds, he followed with: "Is this a trick question?" (Neither of us knew how alike we were in suffering everyone's condemnation.)

"How's 11:00 p.m.?"

"That's perfect. Are you *sure* you wanna do this?" he asked timidly.

What was he talking about? Was he worried that I got ugly and it would ruin the memory? (I hadn't.) Or was he asking if I wanted to have sex? (I didn't.)

"Yes, I'm sure." ●●

7

....

KNOWITALL

Perlstein's retirement never occurred to me. He lived in our neighborhood. He was like family. We weren't going anywhere.

I went to a session one day, planning to cry about some guy fucking with my head.

He blurted out: "Hey Nan, you know I'm retiring, right?" He saw my face. "I could have sworn I sent you a letter!"

As the tears fell, I wondered why he'd send a letter and not just tell me in person, in a nice shrink kind of way. Ease me into the devastation, so it's not so bad.

Months later, I vaguely recalled sitting on the toilet reading a notice, like a wedding announcement, and absentmindedly throwing it out. My brain refused to register 'retirement.' Anyway, I knew *now*.

Perlstein dumped my father while he was still in the hospital. He had to dump him. How else does a psychiatrist leave his dependent patients? Perlstein hadn't been well and was supposed to rest—it's why he had to retire. Some kind of illness. He was taking care of it. He would smile and his eyes would twinkle. He moved near his daughter on the West Coast. Only he couldn't stop helping people and was soon saving West Coast lives.

When he left, he told me to think of him sitting on my shoulder.

We loved Perlstein. He saved us. He often spoke on the phone to my mom, as a friend. He once screamed she needed a brick thrown at her head, to stop her from speaking to her abusive sister. We had Perlstein in our lives all those years, how could we know how great he was? It's like eating Italian cheesecake from Veniero's: when you try it elsewhere, it's not cheesecake. You don't recognize it and you're never going back.

I met my father's first new shrink after Dr. P retired. He was still in the hospital. The stunted fat slob wore a thick gold ring grown into his stubby pinky. He sunk into a worn leather chair that barely held him, behind his cluttered filthy desk.

He was one of those greasy, dyed, brushed-over-last-strands-of-hair guys.

If he can't admit he's bald, how can he save my dad?

My father correctly answered, in one-word syllables, all the questions stubby asked. My dad knew he had to get out of jail, so he answered without any emotion. I detected my father's hatred for this psycho-pharmacologist. Normally my father would ignore such a man. The contrast between the two men was striking: the unaware repulsive doctor against the defeated fully aware patient.

The sickening role my father had to play could not diminish the broadness of his shoulders, or the baritone eloquence of his saddened voice. My father couldn't help but be intimidating. No institution would rob him of his basic masculinity. I was silently grateful. His true essence was still intact. They hadn't broken that. He still had his fearsome bulldog underbite.

My mother was still in constant communication with Perlstein.

He next recommended a well-known shrink at NYU, who arrived at our 10:00 a.m. appointment very excited that he had run his five miles at 6:00 a.m. My father was slumped over in his chair.

NYUshrink was attentive until he found out we had insurance and weren't private pay. He asked my parents to leave the room since my father wasn't speaking. For some reason the shrinks deferred to me, not to my mom.

"Your father will not recover. Sometimes people just go psychotic for no reason. I see it all the time. Let's try ECT."

I didn't ask my father what he thought of NYUshrink, he just came out with it: "Phony."

We went to a $500 shrink—a stuck-up nerd in the coolest part of the Village. We walked down to his office. After five minutes with my folks he turned toward me: "So what *do you do* Nancy?"

It felt perverted. My mother thought he was flirting with me. We paid the $500 and left. I asked my father what he thought of Villageshrink: "Creep."

My mom was referred to Knowitall—a shrink who boasted he taught psychopharmacology.

First he prescribed Prozac again.

This caused 'organic brain syndrome,' so that my dad couldn't understand the difference between broccoli and cauliflower, how to tell time, and other minor major things. It also caused extrapyramidal side effects.

Knowitall eventually discontinued the Prozac but the grimaces took a long time to cease.

Next he tried Depakote, another drug Perlstein warned Knowitall about.

Perlstein was still trying to get my father out of this nightmare. Depakote had caused my father to develop Hashimoto's thyroiditis, when Perlstein first tried it over a dozen years ago. But Knowitall *refused* to believe he couldn't tolerate Depakote. Until my father became violent from it, that is.

He hit my mother and slapped my sister in her face. He started groaning, shouting, cursing, setting off the house alarm, having racing thoughts — waking my mother up all hours of the night and hitting her. My father became completely disinhibited, aggressive, and agitated.

"They should have killed me," he shouted and began throwing things. So Knowitall gave him Mellaril to counteract the Depakote, along with Restoril and Ambien.

I could see the anguish in my father's face — being forced *by us* to take meds he knew were making him sicker.

The Mellaril caused akinesia and dystonia, as my father would stoop over as his legs buckled. He began rambling as his fears escalated. He thought he was dying.

This was most likely a sane thought.

He would take short steps, with his mouth open and drooling.

Discontinuing Mellaril caused him to develop a trance-like syndrome, where he would alternate between pacing the house and shaking his head back and forth for hours. Other times, he writhed in bed all night, completely unable to sleep.

The last drug he was prescribed was Risperdal — "*a great drug*," Knowitall claimed.

Around this time my sister Deanna visited from Utica with her six-month-old son, Jamie. My father shouted to them: **"Get out of here!"**

This also may have been a sane thought, because on Dreck's last visit my father beat me up. He zoomed towards me after speaking with Dreck and pummeled me to the floor.

I was 27, looking up at this lunatic. He was distraught. T looked my way before ducking for cover, checking to see her mom was alright.

My father hadn't hit me since I was 14 and studying for a High School Regent. I was yelling for everyone to shut up so I could study. My father came into my room but I blocked his hands. He kicked me instead. When I tried to look at my leg, I couldn't lift my jeans over the bruise. I pulled my pants down to see a nice rounded baseball matching my knee. I called him a child abuser and he never hit me again.

This time I waited until Deanna and Dreck left.

Deanna met Dreck at the Concorde Hotel in the Catskills. He was 17 years older and said he wouldn't date anyone over 30. She was 29. They got engaged in four months. Then she moved to Utica.

When Leslie and I met them at the Concorde for a reunion, Dreck told Leslie: "You'd argue with any fuckin' thing I'd say." Deanna didn't stick up for Leslie.

Later, when I gave them a T-shirt for my nephew Jamie—Dreck opened the door of their hotel room and threw the gift into the hallway, yelling: "I don't want your fuckin' T-shirt."

It seemed that whenever Dreck was around, my father psychically sensed evil.

After they were gone I ventured into the living room. He was sitting in the orange chair and without saying a word, his right leg started to cross over his left leg and his right arm started to slap his left arm.

"Dad—you can't stop?"

He looked at me, fearful, eyes wide when I got in front of his rigid face—he couldn't speak.

I screamed to my mom.

We called Perlstein on the West Coast.

"Hi Nan, what's happening?"

I cut him off and started to describe my dad.

"He's having a seizure from the Risperdal. Who put him on *that?*"

I called Knowitall, who said: "Risperdal does not cause seizures," while he started blabbing away yet again, that he teaches psychopharmacology.

"Well, he's having one now." *You pompous ass motherfucker*, I thought as I hung up. I called back Perlstein, who reassured me the seizure would wear off.

Aware he might die, my father busted out of the silence:

"SANDRA—*I LOVE YOU!!!*"

I got that brain burn—a split-second confirmation that would make me single forever if I never found half of what they had.

After an unbearable hour, his arm and leg slowed down. But they still moved. He was soaked in sweat. His lids closed briefly and then he looked at me as I cried from relief.

I asked my father what he thought of Knowitall when gravity allowed him to collapse: "He's a shyster and a crook."

My father was now psychotic. It was the lethal combination of Depakote after the Prozac. Then the Risperdal seizure infantilized him—his rational wiring burnt out.

It reminded me of a guy I grew up with. He did some kind of hallucinogen in college and was never the same. It retarded him. But my father wasn't partying when he lost his brain.

He was just constipated. ●●

8

....

TWO DOZEN ROSES

The day I turned 40, Nathan and I drove five hours with two dozen roses for Deanna's anniversary. She opened the front door narrowly enough to take the roses and shut it in my face. Her kids were peeking around trying to get a glimpse.

Nathan said: "You tell me these things, but if I didn't see it, I wouldn't believe it."

He understood my family. In a way he understood me. Nathan was my ex-fiancé, now my friend. We got engaged right before I went to optometry school.

I found a great apartment—but as soon as he moved in—it started. I saw how chaotic his existence was.

Nathan was the first man I never had any problems with. He always took my side. He was never a headache. It's possible that his kindness kept me from seeing the truth about him.

Almost everyone else saw it though.

My dad said: "Do you want to be on Medicaid the rest of your life?"

Perlstein said: "Not for you!"

My mother: "Oh, but she's so happy with him."

Deanna: "Can't you marry Nathan? No one ever played with Jamie so long."

Leslie: "He doesn't like to work. He'd be happy with two bananas, living in a ditch."

We broke up after I learned that he had lied about finishing High School. Formal education was something he didn't value for his life or mine. And because he didn't value it, he didn't support my pursuit of it. He didn't support me as I put in long hours in graduate school. He never helped. Never even asked how he could.

Breaking up with him was a relief, but I felt exposed too. Nathan had always been a buffer to creeps. Letting go of him felt like I was inviting them back in.

Nathan found his way back into my life five years later. Now he would pop in for paid favors—like road trips.

Deanna was scheduled for a brain biopsy that coming Friday. Dreck found a neurosurgeon and wouldn't tell us anything.

Deanna's initial symptom appeared as a reading disorder. She was turning 43 and had never worn glasses. She came in for an exam. I made every prescription I could. I did every test. She couldn't read close.

Normally, I'd tell a patient they needed a CT scan or an MRI, if they presented with an unsolvable complaint. I'd refer them to a neurologist.

I was afraid she'd go home and say: "Nancy's so dumb, she wants me to have an MRI—I hate her."

She went to an ophthalmologist and asked him if she could have a brain tumor. He said: "There's no way."

Then she began to have seizures.

She had become distant since she married Dreck. They never invited me over. Dreck was crossing people off his list. We didn't know he was one of those *Sleeping with the Enemy* control freaks when we met him. No one knew why she married him.

Deanna's only requirement in a man was straight hair. She was petrified of having a redheaded kid with frizzy hair. It had to be kink free. She didn't want her child to suffer the way she had. It didn't matter if he was a moron from Utica, as long as his hair was straight.

Before they moved to Long Island, I took a train to Utica to help with Jamie's Bris. When the Rabbi began the torture, Deanna was hiding. Dreck was helping the Rabbi while little Jamie's piercing shrieks filled the room of relatives eating brunch. I ran through the crowd to Jamie who was lying on the table, while his penis was being mutilated and leaned in hugging his entire upper body and kissing his forehead. He stopped screaming.

The Rabbi did a little song and dance with Jamie when it was over. Jamie had diarrhea for the rest of the day and collapsed in a heap on the bed later on.

Dreck dropped me off at the train station the following day and drove away.

It was one of those desolate stations you'd see in a Stephen King movie. The only people there were ticket booth takers and two to three others I didn't want to get near. No one was by the tracks. Nothing could be seen for miles, except ugly vistas of dried-out spotty nothingness. I found a large concrete beam and stood behind it so no one could drag me off.

The train took two hours to arrive.

When I asked Deanna if she still loved me, she said: "Dreck would have come back to get you."

Now, years later, Deanna forbid me to come over. Whenever I saw her, I arrived unannounced. It was the only way I'd get my foot in the door. They insisted I wash my hands before I sat on their food-smeared couch. Deanna was always the tissue on the floor kind of person—she'd pick 'em up when she got up. She never had a germ phobia before. I was the one who wouldn't shake hands. None of us realized this dysfunctional household might have an ill mother.

When did this thing really begin?

One of her worst experiences was in her mid-twenties. She was going through a break up with some guy and had a panic attack. The ER doc gave her Haldol. When she got home she started yelling: *"MAHHHHHH."*

My mom ran in to see her daughter's head twisting, and her tongue darting in and out of her mouth. Her voice got worse by the second. It sounded like Linda Blair in *The Exorcist* so she stopped talking and began sweating profusely.

My father called the ER doctor who prescribed it. He told my father to give her more, so he did.

Shockingly this is still taught—that when a patient has an adverse reaction to Haldol, it's because the dose is too low.

My father looked in the PDR and started crying. It was the first time I'd ever seen my father cry.

Then he called the ER doc back and said Haldol has the following severe side effects:

'Tardive dyskinesia—fine, worm-like movements of the tongue, or other uncontrolled movements of the mouth, tongue, cheeks, jaw, or arms and legs. Other serious but rare side effects may also occur. These include severe muscle stiffness, fever, unusual tiredness or weakness, fast heartbeat, difficulty breathing, increased sweating, loss of bladder control, and seizures — *neuroleptic malignant syndrome.*'

You do not increase the dose if it's neuroleptic malignant syndrome. It can be fatal.

The doc responded: "That's only 25%."

My father screamed: ***"That's one out of four!"*** I can still hear that scream.

My mother called Dr. Perlstein.

For 12 hours her neck never stopped twisting to the side. Her entire body was drenched in sweat and when she choked out a couple of words with her tongue darting around, it sounded like a stroke victim's worst nightmare.

Dr. Perlstein told my mother she would not die and that it would wear off. Yet if she didn't have a bowel movement, she would have to go to the hospital.

After 18 hours, she voided a small movement. We clapped and cheered with tears in our eyes. Our family would be okay; Deanna would survive. Haldol was a bad drug.

Or was my sister more susceptible because she had a slowly growing tumor?

She lost her sense of smell when she turned 30. A neurologist told her she had a virus. Her sense of smell never returned. These are all piecemeal facts learned long after the events because Deanna stopped talking to me. How little I knew of my sister, when only a few years prior we knew everything about each other.

Before her brain biopsy, my mother begged to let Dr. Arthur Wolintz look at the films. Arthur was a trained neurologist and ophthalmologist we knew for over 40 years. But Dreck refused to have Arthur look at the films. Dreck decided Dr. Breeze was the best neurosurgeon, and gamma knife radiation was the answer.

My mother asked Dreck if Deanna agreed.

"Oh, she can't handle knowing the truth about this."

"You mean Deanna doesn't know about her tumor?"

"I'm handling it," he said.

I consulted with my first attorneys. They told me Dreck was Deanna's automatic proxy by marriage, and unless she made a separate proxy, there was nothing we could do. ●●

(Who's *your* proxy?)

9

....

PIPPI

It was 11:00 p.m. when I walked into one of the fanciest hotels in Manhattan. I couldn't remember the last time I'd been in a hotel. I wasn't one of those NYC women who met for drinks at the Regency, Carlyle, or wherever it was that over 40-year-old women went. I got tired of drinking at 16.

The hotel clerk had a key waiting for me. I wondered if they thought I was a hooker, or if hookers visited him.

I would never have said yes to the date if I'd known I'd be meeting Bram at a hotel. He had torn his Achilles and was bound to crutches and a short travel radius. I rode up to the 49th floor. I rang the bell, instead of using the key.

A man I didn't recognize opened the door and embraced me in a warm half-hug, smiling widely but not looking me in the eye. His face was red and flushed with a light bump on his smooth cheek he never had before—*amelanotic melanoma?* His once firm, slim abs were now hidden under the swell of a hard bloated gut. His hair (still thick and glossy and not a single gray) wasn't an unruly mop anymore, but cut straight over his forehead like a gladiator.

But his smile was a lie. Everything was wrong. Something had crushed him. I sensed a huge oppression—a colossal 500 pound weight on his back.

He was one of the lost people.

He could still be a friend I hoped, as my 26-year vision of him died. I followed him as he marched into the kitchen catching a peripheral scan of his suite—larger than any apartment I ever owned.

He opened the freezer and stuck his hands in a bucket of ice: "I really shouldn't do this, I should use a spoon…Wanna drink?" as he refilled his.

I looked at the half empty bottle of vodka. I never knew it came in that *size.* "Okay," I said, trying to calm my nerves.

It was my first date in two years, even though I kept telling myself it wasn't a date. I liked his hands in my ice. He could take a sip from my soda too—a true indication of how I really felt.

It was Bram.

He had this sexy way of handling himself. He even walked cool. What a relief he couldn't dance—at least there was *something* he couldn't do. He was like Hubbell in *The Way We Were.* Except I wasn't Katie—my infatuation ended years ago. But I still admired him—even if I had lost that feeling.

He pitched a perfect game at camp even though his best friend told him not to try. He was the lead actor in the summer production. The director wanted him to take the lead for the next play, but Bram didn't want to sing.

At law school, his professor commented: "Why is Bram's argument so superior to everyone else's in the room?"

He downplayed his intelligence. It wasn't cool to be that smart. It must have been a burden to be great at everything. Seeing him walk crooked on the beach after drinking an entire bottle of champagne by himself didn't help. Even at 17, I knew I didn't want to wind up with some drunk.

He never smoked pot in front of me, but along with hash, ludes, and everything else, I always knew there wasn't much Bram wouldn't try. This blinded me to the brain underneath it all.

I followed him to the couch and sat on the opposite corner. Too soon, he looked at me, and said: *"I like… love you,"* with his gut rolling out of his shirt. He bent down to give me some cute gift and I saw the crack in his ass. I was so excited to be with him. I couldn't care less he was a mess.

"You look like Pippi Longstocking," he commented.

Was it because having no clothes I showed up in a thin flowered skirt with a five-year-old blouse? I smiled. Maybe he was wild, a drinker, and had lost his way, but he was as warm as could be.

"Won't you kiss me? Please let me kiss you already," he kept begging.

"When's the last time you had sex?" I responded.

"Two weeks."

"Sorry, I'm not kissing you, but you can massage my feet if you want."

So he kissed and rubbed them for two hours, while he bared his soul.

I had no sexual energy, no attraction, and at the same time couldn't calm down. My pulse was racing. I was totally confused.

"I know you better than most people — how many men know you since you were 12? Do you know how cool that is?"

Somehow he was neglecting the 26-year lifetime.

"I can't believe you're sitting here. I can't believe you're not married…"

"I don't believe a thing you say," I said to his many compliments.

As he began to tell me his life story, I forgot about my nerves.

"After my first wife cheated on me, we got divorced. I called someone I knew in college. We had met at a reunion while I was still married and she came on to me. So when I got separated I called her. I should have called *you*."

He gave me a strange look.

We met again for breakfast, even though he never ate breakfast. He ordered ham with eggs.

"Please don't eat *Babe* while we're together."

He scratched his head: "No one tells me what to do."

"Well I won't get near you."

He called the room service back and told them to leave out the ham. When I asked to taste his omelette he broke into a huge grin. "I'd probably get a lot healthier being with you," as he fed me a forkful.

He must have called right after I left because there was a message when I got home.

"I had a great time with you. I just loved the banter back and forth. *I always liked you*."

Bram was the man I meditated to whenever I had a breakup. I would visualize him to regain my self-worth. It never got bad with Bram. I kept a cartoon he drew when I was 17. It was on an old worn-out piece of bag. He drew a picture of us holding hands by a tree with his college address, along with "I'm crazy about you." Of course, this was right after I gave him a blowjob. His *last* blowjob. I wanted to send him away complete.

He called later on from his hotel and felt compelled to share his insight of me without being asked: "I think you could be a lot happier than you are. But you deserve someone who can cook dinner with you every night. Maybe I'm getting a little ahead of myself." He had no idea I couldn't care less about dinner, or about him yet.

On our second date he brought so many gifts I didn't know what to do. I rarely accepted gifts because I didn't want to owe anyone. One boyfriend gave me lingerie. A thong and bra set. My ass looked so good I didn't recognize it. I was too embarrassed and told him it didn't fit and gave it back.

Another man gave me garnet earrings. I suspiciously asked when he got them, knowing something was off. He confessed he had them for years, from a trip to Prague. I got a rash the day I wore them.

Bram's gifts were celebratory. He brought gifts for my family too. It was so much I couldn't carry it all home. He managed to take me to the Waldorf for dinner and walked in on crutches, wearing a T-shirt as if he owned the place. He told me if I got cold to let him know and they'd loan me a jacket.

He asked all about my life, my childhood, everything before we met at camp and everything after. He hardly spoke and kept asking me to continue. The way he was concentrating didn't make me self-conscious. I never felt so relaxed.

"I can't believe you went through all that," he said with a look of concern.

As we walked back to his hotel, he handed me his crutches and threw his arm around me, pretending he needed to hold me that tight. It was the first time in two years I felt a man's strength on me. When we got back to the hotel: "When will you let me kiss you?"

It only takes one kiss for me to get hooked. Partly because I never kiss anyone, and partly because one kiss lets me know how the rest will be. I couldn't afford to lose control yet. I was sitting on the arm of the couch. He zoomed over and lowered me into the corner—*uh oh*.

Before I could stop him he was kissing my neck, using his teeth to gently bite into me. I wanted him to continue—he was doing it right—but he pulled back and looked at me. He smiled. I must have been flushed. Test successful.

He called as soon as I got home and we spoke for an hour.

On our third date, he handed me a small box. It was a gold ring in the shape of a Siamese cat's head, with emeralds for her eyes and diamonds for whiskers. "It's not much," he said.

It was the nicest gift I'd ever received.

Then I remembered my inexpensive necklace he eyed and touched the previous date, looking like he felt bad.

He wanted to know everything going on with my family—*everything*. So I told him. We were sitting on the couch and he started to shake. I thought he was laughing but then I saw tears: "I just don't know if I can do it," he cried.

"I don't need you, Bram. I can handle it," annoyed he assumed I'd want his help.

He shook his head: "That's not what I mean. I *want* to be there. I just don't know if I can—with everything I have to deal with—in my own life. You're going to need someone."

"I'm fine."

"You're going to need someone," he repeated, acting like the big brother.

Having taken in the weight of my family's problems, he was collapsing under it. I told him I'd be okay and he finally smiled from relief and hugged me.

On our fourth date we watched a movie, fully clothed under the covers in a California king. He fluffed up all the pillows and ordered enormous ice cream sundaes with caramel and whipped cream from room service.

"Nancy, I'm just so happy you're here. I don't even care if we have sex—I just can't believe you're near me. It must be hard for you to be happy with what's going on with Deanna. Maybe if you would think of me as family you could. Leslie will find someone."

"Well, I'm really looking for what my parents have—that kind of love," I confessed.

"What do you think I'm looking for? That's what *I want too!*" he said in earnest. ◀●●▶

10

....

A GREAT ARM

I was now in my third year of grad school. My father had regressed to diapers. I was horrified the first time I saw Gladys brushing his teeth. *When did that happen?*

He got used to the daily bathroom trials—hours trying to void—excruciating pain. It was his accomplishment of the day and he seldom uttered a word.

Gladys was huge. She had terrific strength. She would pick my father up off the floor like a feather when he'd crash out of bed. She was his aide.

He didn't sleep in the same bed with my mother anymore. My mother now slept alone on his side of the bed. Everything reversed.

My father would stare ahead with a blank look—like a broken horse. My belligerent, stubborn father who always had to have his own way, would now obey whatever was asked of him. Gladys hoped it would remain so. When I asked if he could try brushing his own teeth she shrugged me off. She said this job changed her life, so she started disappearing on vacations.

My family went through a substantial financial loss during these years. Gladys was not covered by the great insurance we paid a fortune for. If they'd had Medicaid, they would have been entitled to a home health aide. My father hadn't worked in over a year.

My mother kept the practice afloat with their savings — keeping it alive for him. They worked together for 30 years. They never got sick of each other. A low-key couple who had the right life, until it turned upside down. When people asked me how my parents managed working together every day, I said: "They like it."

Their favorite thing was sharing a sandwich on the ride home in the car.

While my father was ill — the optician, secretary and temp ODs treated my mother like garbage and took unknown privileges during her absence. I don't know what feeling sorry for yourself means, but she stayed strong when no one was smiling back.

Some of her friends told her to leave him. She said she was still so happy to have him near. I told her it was worth it and that she struggled for the *Third Entity*. The *Third Entity* is love.

When you have real love, the love becomes its own energy, greater than the two who made it. It exists independently. I told my mom she was doing it for their love. She nibbled her cuticles.

My cat Princy, replaced the life force my mother no longer saw in her husband. Princy became a liaison and great comfort to both of them. He sat on my dad's stomach and would peer straight into him. Then he would proceed to groom him, licking his head everywhere giving him a bath. Just the fact my dad didn't throw him off showed he lost his will.

I got a call somewhere around 10:00 p.m. from Gladys with commotion in the background: "Nancy — the police are taking your father to the hospital."

"What?"

Gladys was out of breath — her voice went up an octave, which made it more ominous.

"Your mother is at Franklin getting her head stitched up."

"What?"

My father was being taken to the psych ward at Nassau Hospital. He had hurled a plate at my mother, almost severing her temporal artery. He could barely move, but somehow had thrown with enough force to slice her wide open. Always the athlete.

Which hospital should I go to? How would I get there? I was living in the city.

Gladys was scared — her calm soothing Jamaican drawl was now a high-pitched moan. I wondered how she could be healthy and that *size*, yet her pulse and BP were always normal. I always took them, in fear that we'd lose her too. But this was too much for her.

I went to my father, fearing they would give him Demerol and kill him like Libby Zion. He wouldn't be able to tell them his meds, or what he was allergic to.

When I got to the hospital, the police and nurses turned me away and said I couldn't see him. My own father?

(I had just read of a famous actress throwing a tantrum when she couldn't get her car deposit back…she yelled and screamed and jumped up and down. She got her money back.) Did I have to have a tantrum?

I did my best and started screaming they better let me in. They weren't budging.

Leslie suddenly appeared, high on coke and smiling that her drug dealer boyfriend was in the same hospital being treated for bladder cancer. Her *new* bartender drug dealer boyfriend. She looked at me funny, because even though she was stoned I was the one screaming. She chuckled and disappeared.

After two hours the superpowers granted me access. He was okay. A miracle. I instantly switched to a calm persona, assuring the psychiatrist I would monitor my father—that it was an accident and to please allow him to leave.

I was petrified they'd keep him.

We were in the end of a long corridor in a very dark metallic office. I peeked into some of the patient rooms. I had to get my dad out of there. My father sat contritely. He knew how to behave among strangers.

I don't know how the psychiatrist agreed to let him go; they must have been full capacity.

We went to pick up my mom. "He has a great arm," she said matter-of-factly.

They were both relieved, exhausted, and victims of something none of us understood. I had to worry whether this selfless aspect of her personality would one day kill her. Like that woman who was knifed to death by her famous schizophrenic fiancé—the one who said he had beaten schizophrenia. I wondered what made that woman *choose* a man who was initially crazy, as opposed to my mother whose husband became ill after 30 years of marriage.

My parents were so frail and my mom appeared dizzy but neither complained of a thing. Gladys adjusted and we were all grateful to be home. But seeing the blood all over the kitchen floor alerted me—to what my mother had endured.

Another month went by. My father became so stiff he couldn't move. He also couldn't speak, eat, or drink. He was suddenly paralyzed. We didn't realize it wasn't sudden though and neither did Knowitall. His diminished talking wasn't so much psychological, as it was the Risperdal causing an end-stage pseudoparkinsonism.

We got in touch with Hatshrink who put him in Columbia.

I certainly didn't expect my mom's reaction: "Nancy—you saved me and Daddy."

"You know, Mom—you're Daddy's one great strength and he's your one weakness." ●●

11

....

BURNING

I had no contact with Deanna for over a year. Dreck would say she was too ill to speak and didn't want to see me. But when my mother told me Deanna couldn't breathe, I demanded Dreck send the films to Arthur Wolintz.

Wolintz called me in the office: "The tumor is salvageable — *move on it Nancy* — Dr. Breeze is a lying bastard. You don't do gamma knife first. You take the tumor out and then use gamma knife only if necessary. The whole thing was done backwards. I have patients living for 30 years after glioma — *30 YEARS!*"

I got an appointment at Sloan Kettering the following week, after putting Dreck and Deanna on my insurance plan retroactively. It took two days.

Dreck let Deanna off on 67th Street, and I saw my new sister.

She was wearing sweatpants like pajamas and they were engulfing her rail thin frame. Her hair was a different color and texture. I rushed to hold onto her as we walked into Sloan. Dreck didn't have the films for the brain surgeon to review, because he sent them via UPS, so the surgeon stuck his head in for two seconds, shook my hand, and never appeared again.

We sat in an office with the neuro-oncologist. She made some comment about Deanna's weight and mentioned scleroderma—my all-time worst nightmare disease and completely irrelevant to Deanna's condition. When I asked her about the tumor she said: "I don't think the tumor is really a big deal to take out—but I have to find out why she's so emaciated."

Right, focus on her weight, not the tumor. That's why we came to Sloan, I thought.

They left Deanna alone in a room—with an AIDS patient, and Deanna's very pronounced fear of germs. This peculiar woman's boyfriend was sleeping over, so I slept over too—all four of us. Neither of us could sleep, and having not seen or spoken to each other for a year, we stayed up all night on her bed. It felt like before. Before she distanced herself, we spoke several times a week.

She wanted to talk about the germ thing. She was trying to figure out when it began. After the twins were born, she developed a huge paranoia. I hugged her bony legs. She was beyond gaunt. It was almost *not* her at all. But her little girl voice still spoke and I got my sister back.

She was going to live! The neuro-oncologist said the tumor was easy.

Deanna was an insatiable reader until she couldn't read anymore. She constantly informed me of new studies and research. She was a gifted poet also.

Having the tumor located in her temporal and frontal lobes greatly affected her decision-making.

None of us ever looked at the big picture of how drastically her behavior had changed over the past few years. We assumed she was nervous being married to a manic guy.

Dreck had gone bankrupt. His millions were gone. They were renting a house on Long Island to escape the humiliation of his creditors up-state. Dreck became extremely bitter. Deanna never got a break. They now had three kids and no means of support. My parents helped them, but never spoke about it out of respect for Deanna.

Deanna was on Lamictal from a previous neurologist and Sloan kept her on it. She started to burn when they put in the IV. But they didn't believe her. Just like they didn't believe that she couldn't move her jaw for over a year; or that her shoulders and jaw clicked. If you leaned in you could hear her shoulder click, as it did when the intern *forcibly* moved it.

No one was kind to her or believed anything she said.

The Chief Psychiatrist came in with a group of interns and yelled at her: "It's *in your head*—the burning doesn't exist!"

But the burning wouldn't stop, and she could barely swallow now. Sloan didn't seem to care she had an operable brain tumor—could it be the way my sister looked? She looked like Eric Stoltz in *Mask*, only worse. Her once glossy beautiful red hair was now brittle with the red faded into a dull burnt orange. Her face was a pale greenish chalk. Her lips were enormously swollen and blistered.

She was extremely ill, and no one wanted to look at her. I couldn't help but think this played a huge role in her lack of care.

She could not eat solid food because her esophagus was inflamed. So she lost more weight at Sloan in her anorexic state. She had to beg for help changing her maxi pads, as she could not move her hands. It was beyond indignity. What woman wants help changing her maxi pads? Did the nurses think Deanna was a malingerer? Or was she just too depressing to look at?

Her hands became so weak she couldn't roll the IV into the bathroom.

She hated being dependent on the nurses and was more afraid of bothering them.

We never heard from the surgeon again, which was the only reason we'd come.

Dreck signed her out after a week. She returned to sit alone in a darkened room, as light pained her. Noise bothered her too. She wasn't able to smile because she couldn't move her jaw. The doctors said she was depressed.

Was she supposed to be happy?

I began to get ill whenever I spoke with Dreck. I don't know why he repulsed me. It was either his upstate drawl or something more sinister. He didn't seem to care. He wasn't doing what he should. Then one day he said: "We never should have gotten married. If it weren't for the kids, I'd be outta here. We never should've had these kids — you know it wasn't easy for us to have them. But I have my responsibilities. I shouldn't be telling you all this."

Before Deanna got ill, Dreck joked: "We lost the marriage."

Deanna would have been happy with a Rockaway guy living in a shack. Dreck was the older creepy thing who preyed on her. His first wife cheated on him — now I knew why.

He was the one who seduced her. He was the one who went bankrupt building two supermarkets when he had a wife and child to think about. He had the crap insurance that his Breeze wonderdoc took. He was the one with the low sperm count, making Deanna go through a million tests to find out what was wrong with *her*. He's the reason she took hormones, which ignited all of her symptoms.

Barry Zide got hold of Pat Kelly at NYU. Pat looked at the films Sloan gave me: "Doesn't look good — I think you should stay until your sister gets here."

I was confused. The neuro-oncologist said it was easy.

"My sister is very weak, would you please speak gently with her?"

"I'm not really good at that—that's why I went into brain surgery. I'm just a mechanic."

Then I looked at the films: "That's not my sister's brain." I don't know how I knew. We peered at the small typed print. It was a 65-year-old woman Sloan slipped in by mistake.

Pat looked at me dreading the unthinkable, muttering: *"Sloan."*

"Let's see what's in the other package," he said with some hope.

This time we looked at the name first—Deanna!

He smiled and said: "Piece of cake to take this out. Why didn't Breeze do it? He had the brain open. I'd just move this here, that there."

Pat was going to remove the tumor and solve her skin condition and joint dysfunction. Pat told Dreck he couldn't operate until Deanna gained weight. Until she got bigger, she wouldn't heal. All she had to do was gain a few pounds. So Deanna stopped eating. HIPAA prevented me from speaking with Pat directly, after Dreck showed up. No one was allowed to speak to the doctors unless Dreck authorized it, even though I was paying for it.

They gave her a feeding tube in case she couldn't eat after the brain surgery. Pat wanted to get her ready. She hated the feeling from the tube. And she was furious. She kept lifting her shirt, exposing her breasts to show me what I had done to her. The vile nurses saw this and laughed.

I've never forgiven myself for allowing that feeding tube. It was a mistake. Her lips were bleeding because the surgeon ripped off her blisters during the surgery. She looked so awful no one looked at her. And she was still burning.

Finally one doctor vindicated Deanna. An ophthalmologist discovered the source of her burning: Stevens-Johnson syndrome from the Lamictal.

The Lamictal was not only causing her emaciation and joint dysfunction, but it was blistering all of her mucous membranes. It was the reason we had to wait to remove the tumor. It was the reason we wasted time with a feeding tube. It was the reason the worst was still to come. And it had been there all along.

They were going to switch her to Keppra for the seizures with an antiemetic for her nausea. But then Dreck said he was pulling Deanna out of the hospital. He complained: "It costs 50 dollars to schlep into Manhattan every day."

That he couldn't conduct his nonexistent business, nor care for the children that were with their invisible babysitter—he lied to the social workers.

I begged him to let her get the tumor out. Otherwise she would have suffered through the feeding tube for nothing. "You can't take her out. I will call the police if you don't let them help her."

He stared me down: "You're a nasty person. You have a nasty personality. You can't help it."

Next Deanna said: "How would you like it if I put burning spikes in *your* body?"

I told the GI doctor if they let her go, we'd never see her again. I thought they had authority to keep her. I didn't know about AMA.

Barry Zide said: "The mother of your children — you don't do every-thing possible? Maybe he just doesn't love her. Maybe that's the whole problem."

Dreck ignored doctor's orders and took her out against medical advice — AMA. This was so unbelievable that it didn't seem real.

Throughout the summer Dreck would hang up on my parents, threat-ening that they'd never see their grandchildren again. I called to tell him I wanted to take Deanna back to NYU. He then told Leslie he was afraid I was going to bomb the house.

I begged Dreck to sign a form so I could continue to keep Deanna on the health insurance for her brain surgery and he could go back to his other insurance. *He refused to sign*, and instead began going to the doctor for a skin lesion on his face.

My mother said: "Why doesn't he leave the lesion — why is he remov-ing it? He's not removing Deanna's tumor."

He continued to go to the doctor for himself, and I got the bills. This started to drive me crazy.

How could I get her back to NYU?

He took her to Barry Pomerantz, our dermatologist, not because he want-ed to discuss the burning but because he was afraid she was contagious.

I said: "If you don't help my sister and take her back to NYU, I'm can-celing your insurance. *Just sign the form* I faxed so I can keep her on for surgery."

"I should schlep into NYC?" he repeated.

He refused to sign. He refused to take her back to NYU.

I had a nightmare:

I was in Deanna's bathroom, asking her to get the tumor out:

"Don't you want to be a grandmother and see Julie and Lara have children? Don't you want to see Jamie turn 35?"

I had no idea how I came up with that number.

In my dream, she was brushing her beautiful long red hair.

She said: *"I'll think about it."* ●●

12

....

FIREWORKS

Soon it was July 4th and Bram and I met for dinner at his hotel. We were leaving to watch the fireworks at my apartment along the East River.

He started making a tall drink and acted like he was going to walk out with it.

"You're not walking into my building with that," I said, genuinely worried.

He didn't say a word but just walked out with the drink poured up to the rim.

"I think you have a little problem here," I said.

He ignored me, walked out of the hotel, hailed a cab—which flew in record time—had my doorman take a picture of us, and never spilled a drop. That cab ride over to my apartment was more fun than I'd had in the past 10 years.

I was in trouble.

Before the fireworks started, he wanted a serious talk. The ice had already melted and he didn't even take a sip. Maybe he wasn't a *total* alcoholic.

"So how do you want to see this play out?" he asked with his eyes looking right into mine, and then quickly turning away.

I hadn't thought that far in advance, but out of sheer curiosity and in response to his serious tone:

"Well, did you have a vasectomy?"

I couldn't imagine anyone wanting more than four kids.

"Hell no! Sally asked, and I told her: 'What if my next wife wants a child?' and she punched me as hard as she could."

"So you'd have another one?"

"With you???" as his smile cracked wide as the sky.

"Yes," I nodded.

We were now facing each other.

"Yeahhhh! But don't think I won't help out. I love the way babies smell," as he rocked our imagined child.

Time stood still for a moment. I leaned over and kissed him for the first time. It was a brief kiss — a thank you kiss. We sat there staring. My brain began to shift. The fireworks and music began. I jumped up and he rushed from the couch without his crutches to hobble behind me. He put his arms around me using my hips as an excuse to steady himself, leaning in closer than he had to and began slowly moving to the music. Before I knew it, his legs were moving behind mine and he was holding me tighter.

Out of nowhere: "Nancy, we've given a lot of money to hospitals, and we know a lot of doctors. It would be a shame if all that money couldn't somehow help Deanna. Please let me help you."

How did he know what was truly important? And how was it too late to save Deanna now that help arrived?

The last time Dreck called my folks, he said the tumor grew around her brain—like an octopus. And Dreck never took her off the Lamictal.

I had to cancel the previous date with Bram when I heard Deanna had tried to swallow a bottle of pills. I had to lie down—I couldn't move.

I wished she had succeeded rather than live in tortured darkness, burning up alive.

I didn't cry, but suddenly felt hot, as he was moving behind me to the music, faster, stronger. I broke off the embrace. I couldn't merge Deanna with the sexual feelings. How did I have this man in my apartment offering to save my sister's life?

Bram called every single day and always lined up the next date. Sometimes he called when I was working, leaving an insecure message like: "I was just checking to see if we were still on for tonight?"

After several dates, he stopped drinking in front of me. I knew he carried it with him and loaded up before. He knew I hated drinking. A few sips of Grand Marnier and I'm done. Two alcoholics can exist, or an alcoholic and a pothead, but it's hell for a straight person. You're not fun. *You're* the one with the problem.

"So will you be my girlfriend?" he kept asking over and over as if making up for lost time. I didn't answer for weeks—because I wanted to keep hearing it.

He said, "I love you" so often it became medicine to my deflated ego.

"I used to always think of you on my way to Inwood to play golf," he shyly revealed.

"But weren't you older when you started playing golf?" I was confused—he had been married.

"Yes."

"So you thought of me years ago when you were married?"

He looked at me: "I never forgot you."

"Then why didn't you try to find me when you divorced? Why didn't you ever reach back for me?"

He gave me a slow cautious look: "I thought you would be married and it would have been too devastating."

My self-esteem was in the gutter after my last relationship. But so was Bram's after his marriages. His ex told him: "All you do is open mail and the only real job you had was selling pizza."

I remember in his teenage years he sold beer on the beach, worked in the supermarket, and took change in a tollbooth. He drove a tiny car. I was so impressed because he didn't have to. He didn't have to do anything. I was impressed he sold pizza.

Yet after he graduated law school, he came back to reorganize his family's company. With his leadership they increased profits more than four-fold. He never bragged to me and often tiptoed when telling me things he was proud of. He wasn't proud enough and never recognized how great his achievements were. I didn't want to pry, but I began to worry Sally was more than verbally abusive.

"Why did you put your hand up like that? Did you think I was going to hit you?"

He shrugged: "I wasn't sure."

I gave him a kiss where his hand had been.

There wasn't a day without mention of Sally.

"I think she might be having some kind of breakdown."

"Why does she have primary custody then?"

"Because I work full time. But if I got married again and had someone to watch them maybe I could renegotiate it."

"I'd do that—but you know you'd have to stop drinking and give up all drugs. How are your kids managing?"

Bram lived next door to his ex on the same property, in a carriage house. He couldn't stop talking about what she did to him and his family. Their divorce agreement stated that neither one was allowed to have sleepover guests. I asked when they last had sex, but I didn't want details.

"The summer before. We played golf and had sex afterwards."

He told me about his other conquests too. One of them was my camp counselor, who I loved; who he had reconnected with not so long ago. "It meant nothing," he said.

He told me about the woman he had sex with in a stairwell. And the woman who drove him home after his Achilles surgery. If I didn't tell him to stop, he'd have kept going.

"You don't need me," I said, sitting on the arm of the couch in his suite.

"Yes I do need you!" he fired back, grabbing my hand.

"Don't get in my way. I'm looking for a family and what my parents have."

"Please, I've been waiting for you. I need you Nancy. And I need you not to flake out on me with all you've got—you're going to need me too."

It wasn't an act, but I wasn't sure what he needed me for.

I asked if he traveled with his ex. I don't know how I knew to ask this question.

"We usually go on a yearly ski trip to Telluride," he sighed, as if it were a burden.

"Well, I wouldn't be able to cope with that. Let's just be friends. I want you to go with them but I just can't handle that if we're involved."

"Nancy, *please*, I don't want to lose you."

Then he began talking to himself: "Maybe it's time for a change. I've been doing this for 10 years. I won't go. I don't want to go."

"Are you going to be okay with this?"

"Nancy, I don't think there's anything more pure than us finding each other again."

He was smiling broadly. It was July, so he had plenty of time to tell them. "I won't go."

He promised three times in succession and we shook on it.

A few days later we were watching another movie, under the covers with those incredible ice cream sundaes. I put the TV on pause. After his screaming, shouting, and release, I put the TV back on.

He called later very paranoid: "Are you upset you did that? Did you want to do that? How come you wouldn't let me touch you?"

I didn't let him touch me because I wasn't in love yet—but I wanted to reward him for how cherished he was making me feel.

Next he became insistent I meet his mom. She was having chemo at a nearby hospital. I thought she'd feel uncomfortable meeting me that way, but he was so happy about it. We walked over from my apartment and as soon as we got there, his father bolted—stopping on his way out to whisper to me: *"You're gorgeous."*

I thought of my father not leaving my mother's side when she was ill. His mother held out her hand and said: "I remember you. I thought you might like to see some of Bram's pictures from his childhood."

She gave me the pictures. She was incredibly inviting.

Later that day, Bram and I were talking about the visit. "My parents liked you so much. They told me they're so happy I finally found someone."

"Oh, let's visit them at home—I'd love to walk on the beach." I hadn't felt sand on my feet in too long.

But Bram was flustered: "They don't usually like the women I know."

Bram wanted a terrace one night, so he booked a room at another hotel. The staff knew him very well and again I wondered if they thought I was a hooker.

While he was washing his face: "Two hours. Two hours, but I was so happy I was coming to see you I didn't mind the traffic."

I just listened. He had no idea how shy I felt.

He turned around facing me: "I'm afraid to tell you, I don't want you to get a big head, but I haven't been *this* happy since the day my kids were born."

I sighed: "But why did you have to get stoned then?"

"The traffic was so intense I needed something."

"What are you *on?*"

"What do you mean?"

"What the hell did you take? You're acting crazy."

"I did a lude on the way over here."

"I wanna ask you something. Try to be honest—Do you really love drugs or is it that you don't like how you feel without them?"

"I guess maybe that's true—I don't feel comfortable without them."

"Okay, I'm relieved you could admit that. That's a start."

"I just wish Sally would leave me alone—she propositions me when she drinks."

"*What????*"

We were still in the bathroom with his hair now dripping wet. He kept talking—"Don't you want a blow job? Don't you want to fuck, Bram? Please fuck me…you fuck me the best."

"What are you talking about? Why would you tell me this?" (I didn't mean *that* honest.)

"The magic's over Nancy; there's nothing anymore."

He had anger in his eyes and a threat had surfaced, where none had been before. After a long silence: "Nancy, I wish you had called me long ago."

"How? — you were married."

"We could have been together sooner. It would have saved me."

A tear appeared in his eye: "I never thought I'd be happy again."

I didn't know how to handle it. I wasn't ready for what he thought we were.

So I just moved in with a boxer's hug to give me time.

13

....

PROPERTY SHARK

Deanna's phone number had changed to an upstate area code. Dreck didn't have enough money for gas to keep Deanna in the hospital, or to help me pay for his own health insurance. But he bought a house.

Was it all a lie? Did he know the tumor was operable and choose not to? Was this easier than a divorce? Why didn't he sue the initial doctor Breeze when he found out the tumor *was* operable? Did the initial surgeon lie, or did Dreck?

The answer is so frightening I force it away.

My mother offered to mortgage her home after Dreck said: "Oh — that surgery could cost $100K."

I told him the surgery would be covered by the new insurance I got. Was he an idiot or a sociopath?

"You know he has this facade — he gets his way," my mom said.

Leslie kept asking: "Why didn't he leave her with us, so we could get the tumor out?"

When Leslie called Deanna's new upstate phone number, Dreck said: "I wonder what's going to be left in your parents' estate for my kids."

"He thinks he's getting Mommy and Daddy's money, Nan. Remember how we worried who Deanna would wind up with? She wound up with the worst one. Don't tell Mom and Dad he said that."

My friend Darlene said: "He can't just kidnap your sister!"

(Sure he can. Who's *your* proxy?)

The few people who knew couldn't imagine my father not riding there and strapping Deanna into the car. They couldn't understand we had no legal power. They didn't understand Deanna's tumor prevented her rational thought. She thought we all conspired to harm her.

Long ago she whispered to my mom: "Don't tell Dreck, but you're my real home."

Maybe she knew all along and didn't feel safe even then.

My mother's 'benign' MS suddenly became fully active. The pain became so intense that her doctor prescribed Celebrex. Then she began bleeding and became anemic. Soon she had an enormous kyphosis and lost five inches. It happened almost overnight. I thought she fell.

"Ma, what happened?" Her rib looked dislocated. Why wasn't she fixing it?

But when I lifted her shirt, I saw my mother would never stand straight again. How many of these moments are met with no words and a hard gulp.

She got a hobbled gait and walked side-to-side in baby steps. She began sleeping 18 hours a day. I would call but she was always taking nap. This took a long time getting used to—my mother disappearing.

My father would not speak of Deanna. He came to work and acted like she didn't exist.

Leslie was on so many drugs that she never saw how ill Deanna was. Leslie was the only one *not* in shock.

Deanna was going to die among people who said 'heighth' instead of 'height' and buttoned cummerbunds backwards. Utica wasn't exactly cultural.

I consulted with different lawyers who took my money just to tell me I had no rights. Our estate attorney dumped me and never spoke to me again, thinking I was crazy for not pursuing a case against Dreck: "I wouldn't let those kids be raised by him," he said.

Another lawyer said Breeze, Sloan, and the Lamictal neurologist were not accountable because Dreck prevented NYU from saving her life when he took her out of the hospital.

What should I do? Any disturbance would cause her to have more seizures. A Terry Schiavo scene wasn't my idea of a successful strategy. Terry's parents never considered what *she* wanted. I doubt Terry would have chosen to have her face plastered around the world. What would Deanna want me to do?

Dreck said he was "running the show." Instead—he ran my sister into the ground.

I could blame Dreck for not loving my sister. I could blame him for building two supermarkets that failed, leaving him bankrupt without great insurance and at the mercy of the only doctors available on his healthcare plan. I could blame him for taking her away without telling us and never letting my parents say goodbye to their daughter. For poisoning their grandchildren against them. I could blame him for being a very angry, bitter and cruel man.

But I couldn't blame him for being born a moron. Every single chance they had to make it right, Dreck opted not get the tumor out. Although my sister was the sicker one, Dreck was just as ill. He was in over his head, and going to cause my sister to lose hers. No one treated Dreck. No one came forth to counsel the husband of a woman who was dying because of him. Dreck wished she'd be gone. One less mouth to feed—a mouth that couldn't brush her own teeth or eat solid food.

A mouth that couldn't stop asking her broken-down husband to do another favor for her. You don't have to be a genius to go for a second opinion.

Their intellectual ability differed so drastically, but that's also what had balanced them. His money, her brains—then they lost both.

Still, as much as I tried to find one (any excuse)—it didn't add up—any good person would move heaven and earth to save a loved one. I fantasized getting a posse together and rescuing her back to NYU.

The last time my parents saw Deanna was in a Long Island hospital. My father said: "I'm going to say goodbye to my daughter today."

When they got to the hospital, Deanna sent them away, saying: "I hate you."

Then we heard Dreck got the kids two cats. Deanna was severely allergic to cats. I waited for Dreck's mother to call my mother and impart some news about Deanna. But she never called. A year passed before my parents spoke to their grandchildren. Dreck stopped by after taking them to visit their friends on Long Island.

None of us could speak about it after that day. ●●

14

....

THE SWITCH

September arrived. Bram's kids were home from camp, so he was no longer free on any weekend. His Achilles also healed. He was trying to get in as much golf as possible after missing most of the season.

I let the first couple of weeks go by because I was having breast surgery. I didn't want to involve him.

Instead, he insisted on taking me. It was one of the best days of my life. That's how much I was falling in love. Or how bad my life was.

The pre-surgical sonogram delineated the fibroma, as the radiologist Dr. Grappell inserted several immensely long needles to mark it. I was surprised when he discovered another smaller but more central lump that was missed on the two sonograms I had elsewhere. They dressed me back up with the needles sticking out of my breast, as Bram chauffeured me next door to Dr. Ansanelli's building. He was so protective.

Bram sucked on a lollipop while we sat in the waiting room with my needles. The staff said: "Your hubby can wait here and we're ready."

Bram hugged and kissed me.

Ansanelli said: "If I take out the smaller lump, it may distort your breast because it's very deep and central."

"Take it out, I don't want it in there," I said, knowing 'benign' lesions can mutate.

I awoke with Bram standing next to me in the recovery room, stroking my leg, sucking on another lollipop. He was asking Ansanelli one question after another. He was intimidated by no one. He wanted to know why he never heard of laser breast surgery. Why was any woman going under the knife if painless laser was available?

On the ride back I asked Bram: "Would you please take care of my cats, if anything ever happens to me?"

"Of course."

"Thanks."

"Nancy, I just got this *horrible feeling*—if anything *did* ever happen to you…"

My mouth dropped open when I saw his face wince as he turned toward me.

When we got back to the city, he collapsed for 10 hours of solid sleep. As I watched him, I fell deeply in love. I was surprised by the thrill I felt lying down next to him. I didn't even think I liked him that much. But the way he spoke to Ansanelli, the wince on the ride back, the way he fell out—it was too much of a turn on.

Still as I lay there watching him, I was relieved he smelled good, that I liked the touch of his skin, that I didn't have to force an attraction to him.

When Bram awoke he sat up on his side of the bed and without turning said: "I can't stand the thought of you with another man. *I can't stand it!*"

He looked at me shyly and suspiciously. *What could he be thinking?* I felt so loved. He wasn't done—he was on a roll. "Nancy, are you sure you're still not infatuated with me from camp—that it will wear off for you?"

"Excuse me, but aren't you being a little conceited here? My infatuation wore off long ago. Don't you remember I broke up with you? You were the one in love with me. I'm still not sure how I feel about you now."

I was scared to tell him the truth but I had to bring him back.

"You're saying all the right things," he said—relieved it wasn't a fantasy.

Later, he repeatedly asked: "So am I the best? Is it the best sex you've ever had? You're the best for me."

I remember an elderly woman explaining what love was: "You have to want to touch their skin."

Bram had what I wanted more than any man. Only the other half was missing. He didn't have my back.

The fact I didn't answer his question wasn't good either. I told my mom.

"Nancy, oh *come on*, you tell him he's the greatest lover in the universe; that you can't even remember anyone else. What's wrong with you?"

I made an even bigger mistake when he asked: "How many men have you been with?"

I told him. I had once tabulated my list of blowjobs. (How can I explain sisters who teased me for being inexperienced? I had to acquire some kind of sexual sophistication.) Even though I think blowjobs are sex, I think it's different than intercourse.

Bram didn't, in spite of him being with so many women. It didn't matter to him that I wished I'd never been with anyone else. He was looking for things—things he could use later—to get out.

One night—before I could stop it—a silent voice screamed: "This is not going to work—he's bringing it over in *that bag*—there's too much for him to make it in time—he's not going to come through."

But this was Bram.

He kept telling me how bad things were with Sally: "I just don't understand why she's so angry. Do you know what she told me? She told me the kids are falling out of love with me and that I better move back into the carriage house full-time. She said I'm too happy."

I had suspicion Sally had him under surveillance but I kept forgetting to care. All the recent hang-ups on my cell, home, and office phone; he complained that she hacked his computers; and when he called from the carriage house—it was Sally's name showing up on Caller ID.

"She knows about us," I said. "She's probably listening to this conversation."

"FUCK YOU SALLY, FUCK YOU IF YOU'RE LISTENING!"

The next time Bram and I met, we went to dinner at an overrated Italian restaurant quiet celebrities liked. Bram drank so much that I cringed when he spoke to the proprietor. He was adamant about eating truffle—the kind they had once or twice a year.

As we walked home we had our first fight. A huge fight. I told him what an idiot he looked like.

"It would be so nice if you would pour me a drink when I come over and have one yourself," he said.

"Well then call all the pothead alcoholic women who would do that."

It was starting. The 'two to four month' *switch*.

In the beginning he was so compassionate. Once he saw I was hurt by a silly comment he made, it stopped him cold: "Nancy, I don't ever want to see that look on your face again."

He cautioned: "If we ever get into a fight, we have to resolve it right then and *never* go to bed angry."

But now he wanted to argue.

Every time a blood test revealed his mother's cancer had spread, he would become sick. "You have to pretend everything's normal, you know?" he would say. But it wasn't normal, it had never been normal, and no one was preparing him.

He also began to slowly reveal more about his home life: "Sally kicked me out last night because I wanted to get sauce from the carriage house. She just started screaming and pushing me out the door in front of the kids. She'd been drinking martinis all day."

They had dinner together? How often? I felt so secure—I never cared to ask.

In the beginning Bram never spoke to his kids in front of me—he would go out of the room. Once I heard: "Ask Mom to see the picture— I sent it to her cell." It was a tiny thing, but the way he said it struck a chord—like a **Huge Gong**. Whenever I heard divorced people speak, they would say: "your father or your mother," not "Mom or Dad."

My mother said: "Run in the other direction," chewing her cuticles. I couldn't imagine my Bram would turn. We were *friends.*

It was a Wednesday. October 11th. A million police cars were jamming 72nd and First. Earlier news had said someone tried to kidnap a kid at the Food Emporium.

The closer I got to my apartment, the worse the traffic became. They really did try to kidnap that kid, I thought.

I turned on the radio: "… a plane has just hit *The Belaire*…"

My building.

They did not say it was a tiny plane. It was 10/11…9/11 repeating. Adrenaline on.

Every street was blocked, so I got out of the car and ran toward my building, but they wouldn't let me get near it. And no cop or fireman could tell me which floor or even which side the plane had hit. I tried not to envision T and Manet burning up alive.

Channel 2 News caught me trying to locate my cats in an ASPCA van they supposedly put all the pets into. I pictured T having a stroke and finding her dead in that van. My cats were everything.

Bloomberg made a TV appearance. I caught it in a Verizon store while I was charging my cell. He said everything was back to normal and that people could return to their apartments. So I got completely drenched walking back there only to find the nastiest cops. They weren't letting anyone up, except the penthouse couple looking for their dog.

The firemen were complete gentlemen, and I had to fight tears when a handsome chief came over to me. There was such a difference in these two species, it made the nightmare more feverish. The firemen had real confidence. The cops seemed frantic over some terrorist rehearsal they didn't want to screw up.

In the middle of all this, I got a call from Bram: "Hi honey—I just heard. Please tell me you're okay. I'm playing golf in Inwood."

He sounded drunk. I didn't hear from him again for hours. Later, "Nancy, my phone died. I went back to Jersey. Please call me."

He played golf for hours and went *through* Manhattan back to Jersey.

It was close to midnight when my super saw me huddled in a corner of the Hospital for Special Surgery. He snuck me up through water-logged hallways and secret elevators—the ones joining the hospital to the residential side.

I spied candy machines I never knew existed.

Inside, my cats were silent. Waiting. I scooped them into their carriers as I had practiced after 9/11, got my terrorist bag, and fled down 24 flights of soaked stairs with my super. I crammed 500 moist bills into his pocket, wishing I had more. For the first time in 16 years my family welcomed my cats back into their home.

I got a call from Bram the next night, inebriated in his hotel room: "Nancy, I got a room for you and your cats. Please come tonight."

Did he really think I would come to his hotel from Long Island with my two cats? Did he care where I slept the prior night, knowing no one was allowed to sleep at The Belaire?

I asked the only other drug addict I knew to listen to his message. "He sounds really desperate, you know, like when you're scared? He's been drinking," Leslie said.

Another month went by. Bram got the Channel 2 news clip, where Hazel Sanchez did the cutest interview, even showing my cats on TV.

I *had* to get that video.

After a couple of repair dates he grew aggressive when I came to his hotel for dinner. He undressed me so fast I was still standing until he placed me gently on the bed. He gave me three orgasms before I even said a word. I got my smile back with those orgasms. It was so easy with Bram.

"Nancy, please don't ever leave me. I've never felt this way about anyone before. Even my brother said he never heard me speak about a woman the way I do you. I couldn't stand not speaking to you all this time."

Oftentimes he would suddenly apologize: "I'm sorry," he would mumble over nothing. When I asked him to stop saying it, he told me Sally would constantly demand: "Say you're sorry, say you're sorry."

I told him: "Say '*I love you*' instead."

Next he invited me to his sisters' movie premiere. This seemed to be a big deal.

"I never invite anyone anywhere," he would claim over and over again.

He arrived an hour late, so we had to rush to make it on time. When we got there, he immediately left my side to say hello to two women he knew. I found out later that he had slept with both of them. I stood awkwardly alone until he came back over, while the women's eyes followed me the rest of the evening.

He introduced me to his sisters—as his *friend*. "This is my friend Nancy. Remember her sister, Deanna, from camp?"

Janet shook my hand rolling her eyes that she didn't remember, didn't care.

Bram said: "You really don't remember Deanna?"

It bothered her that he thought my sister mattered: "We can meet anew," she chided. His other sister Alexa said hello and shifted her eyes quickly away, without a smile. Bram continued to introduce me as his 'friend' for the rest of the night.

Bram and I met the cast later for drinks, at one of those noisy, phony *'in'* restaurants—the kind where you can't breathe. Bram and Alexa began a nonstop discussion for the next 20 minutes, while Alexa filled herself with extremely appetizing shrimp. She never once looked my way. Neither one of them looked at or spoke to me. Bram grabbed my hand under the table, while still ignoring me above the table.

I pushed my chair back to leave, which caused Alexa to finally look at me. "I'm sorry, you must think I am the most rude person ever. It's just that Bram and I never talk. He never calls. How did you meet?" she asked.

Bram interrupted: "We met at camp. You know her sister Leslie once..."

I had to kick him—"I was always too young for him," I deflected.

"Oh right—what 10 years?" she asked.

"No, we're only three years apart."

"*What?* I thought you were younger than me," she looked shocked.

"Nancy's coming to Thanksgiving dinner with me," he said as if she would care.

"Just don't have ONE drink, *not one drink*," she said.

"What do you mean? That's what Nancy says, Nancy will break up with me if I do the tiniest thing."

"Well, just don't drink and drive. I don't like when you drink and drive," she acquiesced.

"Bram, she's saying you have a problem; she's saying not to drink." Not letting him off.

He looked down mumbling. She got up and said: "He likes strong women," and mouthed a silent *"Thank you."*

Bram and I literally raced back to the hotel because the night turned cold. I ordered my usual: french fries, tomato soup, and chocolate ice cream, with extra mayo on the side.

"Why don't you get something else — a little variety," he butted in.

I was so hungry, hurt, and ignored: "Seriously — you're gonna tell me what to eat?"

In the morning he said: "You look like a corpse," as I was sleeping without the fluffy pillow which killed my neck. Now I was both angry and horny. When he got out of the shower I attacked him, giving myself two orgasms.

When I played my answering machine later that evening I heard a completely soft voice with none of the arrogance from the weekend.

He followed it up with a call: "I was wondering, did you enjoy that when I got out of the shower?"

"Of course — couldn't you tell?"

"I just started realizing that being with you makes me realize how abusive Sally has been all these years. *Oh…you make me happy.*"

But I had to explain to him that he ought to have stayed by my side during the movie and introduced me as his 'girlfriend,' especially to the women he'd slept with, that he needed to look out for me and ask if I was hungry at dinner time.

He came over with his head in his hands: "I'm such an idiot, why *didn't* I do that? What is wrong with me?" 👓

15

....

GRATEFUL

"I told my parents you're coming to Thanksgiving and they're really excited. I've already told you they don't usually like the women I know. My dad said: 'Cocktails start at 4:00.'"

He waited for my reply and when I was silent, he said: "Don't you think that's weird that he'd want me to drink?"

I stayed silent, wanting him to figure it out.

He picked me up in a torrential downpour, greeting me at my building's entrance by throwing his arms protectively around me. He walked me to the passenger seat, shielding me from the rain.

"Glad you're coming with me. Don't worry, it won't be that bad. Half the family won't be there. It's probably my mom's last Thanksgiving."

This chivalry—his protectiveness—sticks in my mind because he knew how to do it. He knew how to do it and, so many times, would simply choose not to.

During dinner Bram remarked how Edison electrocuted animals to prove electricity worked. His sister Alexa said: "That's really cool."

Bram paused: "You mean cruel, right?"

She nodded her head up and down smiling: "Cruel and cool."

I surprised myself by keeping quiet—so I could be civil (when cursing was appropriate) after all.

Bram's mother was so ill—I wouldn't ruin their last Thanksgiving together. I was trying to remember how Andrew Vachss defined the difference between a psychopath and sociopath and worried whether a family could have more than one.

Then it was time for a family photo. Bram sighed negatively as we all got up. Without me realizing there could be an alternative, Bram said: "Nancy is family," as he threw his arm around me for the photo.

When we sat back down they asked me if I thought AIDS was a homosexual disease. I thought of my mother biting her cuticles and making one of her clinical comments. This was an incredibly intelligent family—it made no sense. Hearing this made me feel disconnected from Bram's family.

I thought of the adorable boy who came into my office on his skateboard—the little HIV patient I hadn't seen in awhile.

I said: "No… it just penetrates the mucous membrane faster with anal sex."

They switched topics.

Bram's parents were wonderful to me. They included me in every conversation, and asked me so many questions—I wasn't used to it. Then his mom, Iris, was surprisingly offensive: "You're not a real doctor, though."

I was in the middle of a conversation with Bram's dad—he had asked me a question on the rising costs of healthcare and his employees—but I didn't get a chance to respond. Alexa scolded him for talking to me—when he *should* have been listening to his wife, who began speaking *over* our conversation. Next… Iris gave us an assignment.

She made us go around the table—saying what we were grateful for. It was okay they interrupted us. I heard contempt, not gratitude.

Why did Bram's mom want to insult me? Why was his sister so angry at their father? This is Thanksgiving?

I started looking for the exit.

Alexa acted like I wasn't there—never once trying to get to know me. I couldn't force a friendship and would never be so ungracious, not even to a stranger. She looked exhausted, irritated, and not happy to be there. My hope for a new sister was not to be.

One by one, they began describing their incredible lives, children, and successes. What was I going to say? *I'm grateful my sister is dying of a brain tumor; that I don't have any kids; that I don't have a home anymore; and for the TV-watching zombies I used to call a family. I'm grateful I'm working 60 hours a week, while my hands fall off, while all of you wonder which commercial you're going to produce.*

"Any chance you can skip over me?"

As they shook their heads I found something: "I'm grateful for being invited to this nice dinner and for Bram coming back into my life."

I heard a collective *"Ohhhhhhh,"* from everyone as I bowed my head in embarrassment and tears came to my eyes. Bram grabbed my hand proudly and said something wonderful about me being by his side, but I still couldn't pick my head up. Then he went on to say he was thankful for global warming.

Bram was unusually nervous on our drive back to the hotel.

"Aren't the hours flying by so fast?" he said, a little concerned the following morning.

We ordered breakfast and Bram rolled the cart over to my side of the bed, pouring me coffee and spilling it everywhere. He took that cup and poured me another while we never took our eyes off each other. All of this was done in silence. He was wearing his regal white bath-robe, opened and flowing in the front. The silence, his bare chest, the spilled coffee, something was happening.

Then, out of nowhere: "This is getting serious," he said, as he sat up at the end of the bed.

"She's going to be my wife, so she comes first."

I knew instantly what he was doing. He was rehearsing how he'd tell his kids.

I interjected: "We're all equal." ●●

16

....

THE SIGNS

Later in January Bram told me he had a business trip in March—letting me know early. In February, we had a massive argument about his ongoing disappearances.

Then: "You wanna come to Florida with me? We do a Diabetic fundraiser every year. It would make this relationship solid."

That, or he was trying to absolve himself.

I could manage two days away from my office and cats. It was my first vacation in 14 years.

I arrived at the Florida airport to a limo driver holding a sign with my name on it. His company was staying at The Breakers. When I got to the room I felt a huge wave of hopelessness—there was an enormous bottle of vodka, more than half empty.

But when he arrived all sweaty from golf, my excitement led to two orgasms before I could say hello.

Then there was the gala.

I didn't know we would be attending a fancy gala. Bram always left out major details. All I had were shorts, T-shirts, a couple of skorts, and beach sandals. If I had known, I wouldn't have gone. I had no real clothes.

I put on a striped Jean Paul Gaultier sailor top one of my eyewear accounts gave me two years ago. I wore a skort (yes shorts were underneath) not realizing the back was still stitched together from its catalog arrival. When we entered the room among the gowns, someone commented that Bram brought his daughter.

He introduced me to everyone: "This is Nancy, my *girlfriend*," with an enormous smile.

Suddenly he swerved, wrapped me in a bear hug, and kissed me passionately on the lips in front of the entire room. When we saw his mother, she said hello but didn't smile.

They had mini cups of french fries. They had mini pastries too. Mini everything. I sat down to eat my tiny food, bracing myself for Bram's absence. He had to work the room and I knew he liked his freedom. But within minutes he sat down next to me and never left my side. I even saw his hand rising slowly toward my breasts and caught it in mid-air.

It felt so odd to be that happy.

Bram's brother scowled at us and flew across the room. I was too happy and hoped he was just nervous being away from his pregnant wife. But I was getting a strong impression no one liked seeing Bram happy.

Mostly I couldn't understand how Bram's family ignored the drunkest man I'd ever seen. I was aching to ask: "What's wrong with your brother? Your son? Your friend?"

His sister and brother-in-law were curious how Bram and I knew each other but I wished I could ask: "Janet—doesn't your brother have a *huge* drinking problem?"

Instead she told her brother: "Bram, you're always on the cutting edge."

I was dazed from his attention, and wondered if they were all drunks.

It was getting very late, and we still hadn't had any time together. He wanted to take a walk outside. I looked around and wondered how we could leave.

"Don't worry, we'll come back—I want to get outside with you," he slurred.

He looked up at the sky and said: "Thank you God—for bringing her back into my life."

Then he fell asleep standing up and began mumbling proclamations of his newfound happiness intermixed with golf scores. I cringed at the thought of further embarrassment at the party. Instead, out of sheer exhaustion and drug overload, he asked if we could go upstairs. He collapsed on the bed while I watched the new Bond movie.

The next day, his mother reprimanded him in front of others, chiding him for disappearing the night before. I wondered how she would tell a 46-year-old man how to behave. Especially a son who lived a miserable life without love.

"It was my fault, I had to speak with him," as I saw stress lines forming around his mouth.

"Don't take the blame for him Nancy—it wasn't *you*." We smiled. But something had already switched with his mom.

Later on Bram told me: "My mom said you're a bad influence on me."

So she decided to blame me after all? Why didn't Bram stick up for me?

She preferred criticizing her son publicly while she reprimanded him about protocol. He had said he couldn't wait to leave for college.

Is this why he chose the carriage house?

Later that evening we watched the Bond movie again while Bram stayed awake: "One of the reasons I feel safe with you, is I know you wouldn't snoop."

"What are you talking about?" I asked.

"You know—the way Sally and my mom always snooped."

"Well—if I got scared about something I don't know what I'd do."

The only snooping I ever did was trying to find T-shirts Leslie had stolen from me. My parents never snooped on me—no one ever did. Was he worried I'd find his pot, porn, and everything else I already knew about? He trusted me not to look at what he wanted to hide.

I'm not sure he even knew what he meant because he was so used to hiding things. His privacy had been violated. The privacy required to protect the dishonest relationships he embraced.

His next worry: "Isn't it awful when you have sex with someone and you really don't want to?"

"What are you talking about *now?*"

"You know when you feel you have to please someone when you don't want to—haven't you ever done that?"

"No. You mean you've been with women who weren't into it?"

"Maybe," he said, looking down and then braving my eyes.

"I wouldn't ever have sex unless I wanted to. I mean—maybe I had sex when I was lonely and not in love, but I wanted to. And I'd always want to with you—so don't think about this anymore."

"Okay, I'm glad." His smile made me see him in a new light. In spite of all Bram's pain, his strength made it hard to realize how hurt he'd been.

"Nancy—what have you done to me?"

"I haven't done anything."

"You've changed my life—let's start now—let's start having a family right now!"

When March came around, Bram went to Wisconsin on the business trip he kept telling me about for months. He didn't call, but sent frequent texts about how much he needed to see me when he got back.

His texts became more intense toward the end of the week: "I really think we need to see each other right away, if we're going to be partners…WHY ARE YOU NOT ANSWERING ME?" while he was completely unavailable.

When Bram did get back, he arrived three hours late. He missed a Roy Haynes concert at The Vanguard—one I had paid for. I watched the door all night, until five minutes before the show ended, I saw a guy in a baseball cap trying to talk his way in. He made his way to the wall I was against and began showering me with affection—both arms around me, enveloping me around a beam.

He leaned in and said: "I want to marry you."

He would not stop hugging me.

In the elevator ride up to my apartment at 2:00 a.m., he hovered over me and whispered again: "I want to marry you."

When we got inside my apartment, after jumping up and down about how fabulous Haynes had played, I asked: "What were you doing, that you couldn't phone me once all week?"

He said: "I think you should sit down," not looking at me.

"No, I'm not sitting down. You weren't in Wisconsin, were you?"

It was only then that I realized—it never occurred to me that he had been lying the entire week.

"I went on a ski trip to Telluride with Sally and the kids."

He continued to speak but I couldn't hear. The world around me had gone silent. When he revealed his great premeditated lie, the story he had embellished for months, never once considering how much worse it would be for me to go behind my back. I didn't react well.

No one ever lied to me that way. My brain felt hot. That's what happens when reality is too hard—my brain feels like someone's up there cooking.

I went on a silent rampage, gathering everything he gave me, trying to get him out. He slumped to the floor with his head in his lap, sobbing "I want to marry you," over and over again.

His way of proposing?

I kept opening and closing the front door, urging him to leave and checking to see if the invisible neighbors could hear his sobs. But he sat on the floor, not moving. He refused to get up.

I threw out so much stuff that a small hill appeared in the hallway, with his towels on top. He had given me all his favorite T-shirts by now. I ripped our favorite picture from camp into tiny pieces in front of his face.

He watched in horror at what he had done to me. It was so classic it didn't seem real.

He thought it was fine to lie for months.

"I didn't sleep with her, we had separate rooms—it was the worst vacation I ever had. Now the kids know we're never getting back together."

Now they know?

The more he spoke, the more real it became.

He went on a trip with Sally and the kids, like they were still a family.

"I couldn't call, because I knew I'd have to tell you where I was, and I couldn't do it."

I went into the bathroom—I had to throw up—but my throat was so dry I only gagged.

Finally he went outside and sat on the mound, pleading with me to let him back in.

What a joke I was. How could anyone get this sick from someone lying to them. How much fun it must have been for Sally to hurt another woman—it was the very thing she lived for.

It grew quiet.

After waiting an hour and hearing no noise, I opened the door. He had gone, leaving the entire pile of junk for me to clean up.

I always took great care not to be lied to. I even expected that Bram would do something that weird and tried to circumvent it by asking him not to. He didn't have to promise and agree. He could have said he was going traveling with them and not lie to me. He could have said we should wait until he was out of the carriage house.

He could have protected me.

I kept seeing his face... the look before he went on his 'business trip.'

So that's why he paused and *hesitated* when he left. He had paused after we kissed goodbye and looked directly at me. I was smiling and then grew concerned: "What's wrong?"

I knew now that he wanted to say something. Now I realized it was a look of ambivalence and apprehension—the look of someone who was lying before the lie would happen. Lying to someone he didn't want to lie to—someone he felt close to, someone he *knew* he was betraying.

The *weight* on his shoulders came from his familiarity with deception. The 'micro expression' that I missed but didn't miss. His wavering moment—his opportunity not to be a scumbag—and his split-second decision to continue the betrayal. The betrayal he had been planning, calculating, omitting for a long, long time.

I didn't want anyone to hate Bram. Finally I gathered the courage to tell Leslie, but she understood:

"It's okay Nan, I get it—you don't have to explain. It's too out there, for words. When you lie in business, that's really bad; but when you lie in a personal relationship, it's on another level, and much worse. Yeah, I knew that kid was going to have trouble. Everyone was using him and he couldn't tell. He was the happiest kid I ever saw—always smiling. I can't believe he did this to the two of you."

I still hoped Bram from Act I was coming back. Then he wrote this poem:

I smile when I think of you
though our road's been kind of rough.
We have something special
why isn't love enough?

Did we really know each other
in another life?
Were you my friend and lover
Did you become my wife?

We look so happy in that picture
thirty years ago.
Were we feeling something
from a life we used to know?

Finally he admitted: "There's nothing more important than being able to trust someone in a relationship. I can't stop thinking how happy you were after the Roy Haynes concert and then—the change in your face—that I did that."

For the twentieth time, he promised he would never do anything like that again; that if he'd known how I would have reacted, he never would have gone in the first place.

But I worried he was buying more time until he *had* to lie again.

I knew his environment at the carriage house would never allow him to break free of its toxic waste.

Like the Stanford prison experiment, he would only become healthy once his living conditions changed. ●●

17

....

TAKE MY HAND

"You know Nancy, it took God only seven days to create the world, and you're taking three weeks to talk to me. I never ever would have gone if I thought it meant losing you…please, please, *please* give me another chance."

We went to our new couple's therapist. She wore dark sunglasses and thought she was in a Kim Novak movie. She was a hot broad, who wore so much makeup, I could never take her seriously.

She tried to explain to Bram that lying wasn't going to work with me. "The justification doesn't matter," she said.

He didn't seem to understand that lying ruined trust: "It wasn't lying because I admitted it right afterward. If Nancy didn't overreact none of this would have happened. Why can't I travel with my ex-wife and kids? I *had* to lie, otherwise Nancy would have married some guy and had kids with him."

Bram's truth would change, depending on what the truth was at the moment and how he perceived it to be. Every time I tried to break away, he'd pull the guilt strings. I would see a strange look in his eyes, but was never sure.

Now he wanted me to go on a vacation—with him. Sunglasses encouraged me—she thought there was still a chance. Andrew Weil was lecturing at Miraval, so it wasn't purely a vacation. At least that's what I convinced myself.

Bram lost his cell at the airport. I believe this played a major part in the success of our trip. Fate on our side if only for a few short days.

When we got off the plane I asked: "Is that for us?" as we approached the longest limo I'd ever seen.

"Nancy—you mean so much to me—I want you to have fun for a change."

We drove through the Arizona desert at 3:00 a.m., making out in the back of the limo.

The next day he nervously asked: "Would you be angry if I just relaxed today?"

I sensed he was used to the answer being yes. "Please do. I love when you're resting. I'll see you later."

He smiled, waving his mini fan around his face and reading his novel.

We stayed in a casita at Miraval—the Presidential Casita. There was a separate door off the bedroom out to the veranda and at sunset a kind of mystical light would shine through, enveloping us in natural pink glow. While I walked along the streams that seemed to flow everywhere, I tried to accept that I was on a vacation with a man I loved.

Bram and I took a long walk through the desert. It felt like our own private safari with postcard worthy mountain views—the clearest air and horses far away. Bram smashed a plain-looking rock against the ground to reveal a deep red mosaic within. We spied a family of cows and backed away slowly when a bull began focusing on us. Bram stopped to build a tall rock sculpture—something I would have never thought to do. Then he asked a stranger to take a picture of us.

At dinner he took his napkin and started drawing. He turned it around to show me. It was a ring design. He brazenly told the waitress we were engaged and pulled me onto his lap and kissed me. He made her take a picture of us too.

Making love that night, he waved a wand over my belly, hoping I conceived. "Put your tush on this so it gets up there," as he placed two pillows below me.

The following evening he called his mom: "Mom, I really care about Nancy."

Bram repeated her response for me: "'Well, I really don't know her Bram…Do you think she's strong enough to deal with Sally?' I think because Sally's so mean…my mom's just worried for you."

When Bram and I first met, she was so happy for us. Now that she knew me, she didn't know me well enough.

I got a feeling in my stomach.

Bram finally played golf one day and asked me to visit him there. But I got too busy with the horses, massage, and swimming. I never imagined he'd get so upset. I was used to him not caring how little time we spent together. For the first time he was waiting for me and I didn't show.

The day we left he played golf in the morning. He borrowed someone's cell and called home. His son had suffered a concussion from a sports injury. Everyone had been trying to reach the parents.

Sally went away for the weekend after finding out Bram did. She didn't want to come back from a flower show an hour away. She said the nanny was with the kids at the hospital.

Bram didn't drink, smoke or have any nightmares for four days, but after speaking to his ex—he grabbed a bottle and started guzzling. He brought it into the limo on the way to the airport and continued to drink. Right then my hands started blistering and turning red. I had run out of Purpose Soap and used some of the resorts'. Bram immediately dropped the bottle and began searching through his bag. He gave me some hand cream. When he saw my relief, he forgot about the bottle!

I'd never seen the shift so clearly. All he needed was two minutes of healthy—to escape from what he was returning to.

What mother doesn't run to her unconscious and injured son?

On the plane ride home, he looked at me: "What's wrong?"

"How did you know?"

"I know your vibe."

"Everything's going to go back to the way it was," I said, facing it. He'd show up Tuesday nights and leave Thursday mornings.

He tilted my face to look up at him: "Let's do it—let's get married!"

We locked hands as the plane took off. I got up mid-flight to go to the bathroom. When I came out he was standing there. He grabbed and hugged me while all the flight attendants smiled. People were staring as we parted at the airport—I think we were smiling too much.

The very next day: "I think I should come over and ask your dad for your hand. I want to do this right."

I hung up the phone in a fog. Was he really doing this? He walked into the office, sweating profusely. He hugged Morda and gave her a gift. I took him into the back and said: "Dad, Bram wants to speak to you," and ran out.

After half an hour I ventured back and saw my father sitting there silently, while Bram was going on and on about how he would take care of me, how much he loved me, and that he'd try to make me happy.

"Dad, what are you doing? What are you making him go through this for?"

My father said: "Well, I have to think about it," with less of a smirk than I'd have thought. He pulled me aside: "Is he anything like his dad?"

"What do you mean?" I asked, truly curious.

"I met him at your camp on parents' day. He came on to Mommy. Is Bram like him?"

The entire thing was unreal.

"Dad—thanks—*thanks* for not caring about his money."

My dad looked at me like he didn't understand how it could be otherwise. "Nan, are you sure?"

"I don't know. He's got a screwed up life but he's trying to fix it. He's the only one it feels right with. Mommy likes him…"

Bram looked a little flustered but glad for the break when we returned. Then Bram told my father: "We're not getting married right away."

He meant he had to break free of the carriage house, but I wondered if he was also trying to entrap me, just in case he never would. My dad decided to play along.

When Bram and I went to dinner that night, my father called and gave his blessing. He did it because my mom said: "Lenny, call right now— what's wrong with you?"

(He always knew a phony when he saw one.)

We paid a visit to my folks a couple of days later. My dad opened the door wrapped in one of Bram's white bathrobes. Bram had brought it when he asked for my hand. It was pure Lenny. Bram broke out in a huge grin. He wasn't used to the informality, or the magnetism of my father.

My mom was able to hobble into the living room. She was wearing lipstick.

It was the first time since I was 27 that the man I loved was in the same room as the family who meant the world to me. We all stood up and Bram put his arms around my folks and said: "My new family."

Then Leslie made an appearance and hugged Bram a little too much— laughing the whole time. Later on she called: "Nan, there's something wrong with him—he shouldn't look like that. He looks like a drug ad- dict with that shirt. He shouldn't be wearing ripped clothes."

Have you seen yourself lately?

"Don't let him do whatever he wants—you've got to get him help. Take his blood pressure too. Now—don't wait."

"Get him to Perlstein on the West Coast," my mom chirped in the background.

Leslie continued: "Nan, I'm sorry. I'm so sorry I messed it up for you.

I never knew—never saw you two together. I can't believe I stopped you from calling him years ago. God he's so fucked up now. What the hell happened to him? Oh, sorry—he's not that fucked up. You better do something though…you know he really loves you, but I don't know—it's gonna be really hard for him to be happy without drugs if he's doing that much. Oh—sorry—I'll shut up."

Later at my apartment, I took a chance: "Bram, I'm worried if we stay engaged for years, you'll never *want* to get married."

He looked at me with a soft expression on his face.

"I'd never do that to you, *Nancy*."

18

....

THE WHISPER

Things started happening fast. The week we got engaged, his family had a Mother's Day event. Bram didn't want to tell anyone we got engaged while his mother was so sick but he invited me to meet his kids there. I didn't want to go. I had a bad feeling. I wanted to meet his kids in a quieter setting. But Sunglass encouraged me to go.

When I arrived, Bram's sister Janet was heading downstairs and didn't say hello. His mother got right up and asked me to take a walk through the gardens. She started saying: "Bram is always late."

I regrettably mentioned that I was more worried about his high blood pressure. I didn't know I was being interviewed.

I wanted to talk about his drinking and substance abuse, not his lateness. Soon it would really be *too late*. I had a foreboding feeling Bram might not survive her passing. She said: "That's unacceptable to be so late," excusing herself without asking me about his blood pressure. Was it the chemo drugs?

When Bram arrived he gave me an enormous hug in front of his daughter, who watched awkwardly from above. I felt terrible we weren't introduced first. But I was greatly relieved he showed such bold affection. It seemed so easy.

We walked onto the grass and out of nowhere someone crept up *close behind me* and whispered out of earshot of Bram: *"We're going to take a picture with everyone, and then family only."*

It was Bram's dad. Bram hadn't heard him and when I tried to pull away, he got a tight grip on me. He didn't realize what was about to happen. I pulled and pulled but he just thought I was being shy.

Bram started pulling me toward everyone, who were already in photo formation. *So they were waiting the entire time for Bram to show up to do this? They all knew they were kicking me out?*

Bram and I were on the edge and Bram wouldn't let go. After the first picture, a cacophony of voices rang out:

"FAMILY ONLY! FAMILY ONLY!"

Bram protested: "Nancy's Family."

Alexa turned around without looking at me and shouted: "Don't upset Mom!"

Bram repeated: *"But Nancy's family."* He was pleading.

And again Alexa turned around yelling at him. He let go.

I walked away in a daze—I had been in it since the whisper, but like a person coming up for gasps of air, something inside of me assumed Bram would return to console me. He did not come over.

Instead Bram and his mother paraded along the grounds, walking right by me, holding their hands together rigidly up in the air as if in victory. The formality of their walk coupled with their coldness felt like another dimension—*what the hell was this?*

I tried to get into the house, but the door was jammed. It wouldn't open. I walked to the edge of the grass, but the drop was too high to jump to my car. I thought maybe I could go on the beach and come up around the house, but there seemed to be some kind of gate. No one made eye contact with me. Not a single person came over as they grouped around a table with their backs to me and began eating. After 20 minutes, the door opened when someone came out.

I wanted a clean getaway. I had to get to people who loved me. I prayed no one would cross my path and tried to become invisible.

After 30 minutes I heard Bram: "Has anyone seen Nancy?"

He found me in the basement getting my own mom's Mother's Day cake from the other refrigerator. I was finally able to leave.

"Please don't leave. Please don't go."

"I don't belong here; I can't stay."

He begged and begged and I couldn't win. I knew if I left they'd hate me for ruining her last Mother's Day. I didn't know that's what Iris would have preferred, that she later criticized me for remaining when Bram was late.

I forced myself to eat cake with Bram, who held my hand so tightly that I had no chance to bolt again after his brother marched in with an enormous cake proclaiming: "This is for all the *mothers* in the room."

When they started talking about redheads becoming extinct, Bram said:

"Well, Nancy's sister has red hair. If Nancy and I have a child, it could have red hair."

I cringed. But when I looked up, the matriarch was smiling at me from across the room — the biggest, warmest, longest smile that went on forever. *Huh?*

His son stopped eating, shook his head angrily, and then began eating again. His daughter's fork paused midway through a bite, as she forced herself to swallow it. I wanted to say: "Don't worry he didn't mean it—he loves you the most, and if we did have a child, he would still love you more than anything."

What could I say? I had just met them. I'd just been kicked out of a family only photo. Now Bram was saying we might have a child. I felt dizzy and elated at the same time.

We broke up the next day.

I urged him not to say a thing about their behavior. The following day I got an email: "Nancy—please read my email. I told my parents we're engaged." But that's not all he said, as I got sick reading it.

The letter read: "I asked Nancy to marry me. Nancy wanted to set a date, but then I realized I wasn't ready to leave the carriage house."

The letter did not convey Bram's pursuit of me, or his relief in finding love. Instead it portrayed me as the more eager party initiating marriage. Then it got much worse when he called:

"Nancy, I don't think this is going to work. My mom doesn't think you're the right woman for me. She said I need someone strong because you stayed when I was late."

How could I tell them I loved when he was late? How could I tell Bram his mom was complaining about *him?*

I went to Sunglass, who could not admit that her advice was poor: "His mom wants him. She doesn't want to share him," she said with a cute frown. ●●

19

....

OXYTOCIN

I often think about the narcissistic brains I've known and tried to find the lesson. Why did I give so much to men who could never return the friendship unless the scales were tipped in their favor? How could I find givers and not takers? Why did those who were givers have to make me feel weak? And what was wrong with their mothers? I always blame the mother—it's hard for a warm mother to have a creepy son.

We all need praise. We need to feel loved. But some mothers don't have enough love (or oxytocin), while some deliberately choose to withhold it.

When oxytocin deficiency starts in the womb, these babies are born without the emotional depth to even become narcissists; they're just plain defects.

It's awful because they act fine; they just don't feel. Those *'off'* people who never cry. (Like Bubbles: "I never get lonely.") It's almost a form of emotional autism. They're rigid and 'know' best.

The worst cases are the financially indulged and emotionally neglected. Money and gifts replace love and nurturing. They get it at both ends. Entitlement and zero awareness. They're not fun to live with, unless they see you as an object to enhance their image. But your worth fades when they need something shinier. The mirror becomes mommy.

The sensitive souls who grow up with a mother who *decides* to be cold—usually self-destruct. Emotional neglect can be worse than physical abuse for a boy. They're always not good enough. These beautiful souls have the feelings, but there's no place to put them.

Nathan was left in the crib until he was three, but he has more compassion than a saint. A saint who spent most of his life stoned though. His mom was too ill to nurture, but somehow her warmth got through. Still—her neglect left an imprint. Always looking for the mother he never had enough of, he gives 100% of his heart, but his contribution is limited because he can never be in any environment long enough to succeed. He will never be stuck in a cage again.

Then there is Bram.

"Nancy—you know why I'm afraid to get married? Both my wives turned on me, and I'm afraid you're going to do the same." (How did it get turned around? He's the one who came after me.) "And you're right—like you said—I married my kids to avoid working through my problems with intimacy. It's been all my fault. You know my mother never picked me up. My parents read that Dr. Spock book that said never pick up your crying kid."

"But didn't they pick you up when you weren't crying? Just to hold you?" I asked.

"No. They never picked me up."

Then I remembered how he and his mom walked with their hands clasped tightly up in the air. Was that always how it was? Would he ever get to give her all the hugs he had stored up for her…hugs he needed from her too…before time ran out?

"But Nancy—please, *please* don't ever hesitate about asking me for money. I know you're too proud but I have a lot and want to help you.

Maybe things can work out for us someday."

He was too unworthy to be held, so he found himself not one, but two wives who continued his childhood banner, happy to withhold affection. Happier still to inflict their own cruelty.

And he had found me. Someone whose own mother couldn't put her down. My strength was confusing to him—because I used it in his defense. My compassion was painful—because he didn't know how to receive it. My intimacy the greatest turn off—because what he needed, he rejected.

So he did what he always did—tried to give me the world—instead of himself. ●●

20

....

ENCHANTED GARDENS

In a few days Bram called: "Nancy—I'm sorry. I confronted my parents again. They did it to me, not to you. They wouldn't have done that if one of my sisters brought a friend."

A few days later the diamond dealer sat in the back of Bram's Range Rover on 47th Street, as Bram wrote checks for the loveliest diamond I chose. Then we walked to Rockefeller Center to celebrate. He kept stopping to take pictures of us with his cell.

"You know Bram, my mom read the same book but thought Spock was nuts. Maybe your folks just used it as an excuse...I mean they still seem kind of formal."

"I don't know," he said, with no trouble wrapping himself around me in view of all.

He told me to look for a home. I offered to live in my building in Brooklyn but he frowned. He said my apartment was a dump.

When I asked if he wanted to get a home like my folks he said: "I'll get you a nicer house than *that*."

The next month we went house shopping. I tried finding something impressive. He continued to surprise me with his eagerness for a new life: "I never felt right saying I lived in New Jersey. I want to come back to my roots."

I felt closer to him than ever.

We found the perfect place 5 minutes from my folks and only 20 from his. He had lived in this neighborhood before his ex asked him to move out-of-state. The house was spectacular, with lush gardens winding down a long driveway and secluded from the street. It was a Spanish themed home with rich woods and fireplaces in several rooms. There was a freeform swimming pool completely hidden from onlookers. I fantasized what we'd do in that pool.

It was just the kind of place to give Bram tranquility. It was close to his favorite golf course too. The only thing I'd have to change was the car-riage house it came with—I'd rip it down.

He grabbed my hand and ran with me across the grass to get away from the brokers. The broker gave us a 'nonbinding' statement to sign. I thought nothing of it.

Bram gave the form to his best friend Pects—the lawyer and accoun-tant for his firm. Pects then forwarded it to someone else because he thought it looked suspicious. It was an actual binding contract hook-ing us in without escape. When I questioned the broker she denied it and said it was just to prohibit other buyers from viewing the property. This was the beginning phase of Bram doubting my judgment. I sensed a shift in his attitude toward me.

Bram always had me on a pedestal—and now that we were moving forward, it wouldn't take much for him to knock me off.

The inspection showed we had every chance of being electrocuted in the garage, that the home was infested from different points of 'ingress,' along with substantial mold for my asthma. I got no credit for finding this great inspector.

Before the inspection Bram was deciding which stocks to sell to buy the home. I sometimes wonder—if we had used the inspector the broker had suggested. If we had bought that home, altered his environment, knocked him out of his 'comfort zone,' would that have changed his path?

Leslie always said: "One thing changes everything."

All the defects were correctable—both human and structural.

We continued going to therapy and soon I learned of Bram's greatest 'out.' He said he forgot. He forgot for over a year. I knew the divorce agreement stated neither one could have sleepover guests, in spite of Sally's dates often staying around for breakfast. What he forgot to tell me was that if either one remarried, Bram could no longer live in the carriage house and he'd lose unlimited access to his kids.

It sounded like the agreement meant his new wife wouldn't be able to live in the carriage house *with* him.

I had always told him to stay there as long as he wanted. I didn't see any difference between having our own home to share instead of a hotel. Sally would want him staying at the carriage house even more, thinking it would disturb me. He'd have the same amount of time with his kids. But he couldn't see any of this. He couldn't see he was the one with the power.

I told him: "My mom says you'll never leave the carriage house."

My mom's comment had a huge effect because later that night he sent me an email:

Hi Nan:

I love you and want to make this work. I don't want to lose you. I want to make you happy. Us being together is so important to me, that I'll give up the carriage house for you. You have to admit this is much more than a compromise. Giving up the carriage house and having to see my kids on some schedule makes me want to cry but losing you would make me cry worse. I hope you can feel my love and I really hope you love me as much.

Your Fiancé,
Bram

I showed my mother the letter. She began chewing her cuticles: "Nancy, it's a lot worse over there than you realize. He never should have had kids with that woman. I understand he wants to be there for his kids, but what's the point if he's using? He's just crazy and you won't admit it. Look what happened to him because you broke up with him."

We were still in therapy but Bram was not the same. I wish I had ended the counseling then. I asked our therapist: "Doesn't he *look* funny? Don't his eyes look *really strange?*"

"I try not to judge people that way," she said.

I knew Perlstein would have taken one look and known the problem.

Bram started second-guessing everything I said—intimating that my perceptions were wrong. If I told him someone was rude to me, he would insist I was the rude one. There was a menacing garage attendant who alternated enormous smiles and sneers. He'd take 2 to 20 minutes to get my car, depending on his mood.

One day Bram told the guy I was having surgery. I asked how he could tell that creep anything about me.

"Seems like a nice enough guy to me," he said.

He'd apologize when I'd confront him. He said he'd stop doing it. But every time we met, the first 10 minutes were a test of dominion. Bram doubting my radar—not respecting my take on things.

Before all this, I had once defended him to the management of a hotel. He was amazed: "You stuck up for me—no one's ever stuck up for me before."

It also happened in the car when another driver was cutting him off. I said something to the other driver and again Bram was astounded:

"You stuck up for me—no one ever does that."

Tiny things no one ever did for him that were automatic for me.

While we searched for a home, we rented an apartment for a two-month summer lease. The day we moved in, he ignored me. He sat at a table with his back to me and never spoke a word. It was our first Sunday together in an entire year. The last time we spent a Sunday together he insisted on buying me a dress since I didn't have any. We walked to Saks 5th Avenue and he picked out dresses for me and came into the fitting room, closing his eyes while I tried them on. Two women glanced our way because Bram was paying so much attention to me— if only they knew how rare it was.

When we went to pay he decided to get me a Saks charge card in my name.

Back at the hotel: "Why was that so much fun? I can't believe how little time we spend together. *Nancy, I'm sorry.*"

Now on our second Sunday in a year I left for a walk and when I came back, he was still sitting in the same position. He hadn't moved. He didn't turn around. I didn't confront him. It was too weird. Somehow we pretended that day never happened.

The following month I had another shoulder surgery. The night before the surgery he smoked a joint and said: "I never had a real wedding. Maybe we could have a Rabbi."

I was surprised. Bram hated religion, but he was smiling.

The next morning he walked me over to the hospital and left before I went into surgery. When I got home the next day, he set me up with grapes and water and left for work. He didn't return until 1:00 a.m. and immediately fell into an online poker match. Maybe this was just Bram and I didn't know until we moved in together.

The following day he told me we weren't getting married, that there was no wedding and that he was leaving to go play golf for the day. When I told him he said he wanted a Rabbi the night before, he said:

"That's ridiculous, I don't care about religion—I'm an Earthling."

I left an hour later, lugging my overnight bag over my good shoulder while he ran after me, trying to grab the bag away from me. He called repeatedly over the next few days trying to explain what happened. But I felt sick.

Lewis said: "He's not interested in a relationship of equality; it's too unpredictable."

I asked: "Why wouldn't he want someone he could count on?"

"He doesn't know what that is."

"I don't want to lose you. Please don't leave me." Lines he repeated over and over during all of our separations. Lines that always pulled me back. He continuously demanded: "Love me unconditionally."

But actions aren't unconditional. Unconditional love is unrequited love—real love is between two people who give a damn.

The awful thing about unconditional love is when you have it, you can act terribly—the way I often acted with my family.

But in romance, how can anyone want unconditional love without being loving? ●●

21

JUDY

Some pains never go away. They come unexpectedly if I've had a rough day. Nightmares of betrayal, warning me it's going to happen again.

When I was 26, I learned how to knock someone out in less than three minutes. It was a street fighting course I signed up for after a young girl in my neighborhood was brutally murdered. Learning to street fight felt more appropriate than 'self-defense' after what happened to her.

I could fight for others, but rarely for myself. The idea of self-defense was something I had beaten out of me when I was five.

The bully up the block invited me to his backyard to play in the snow. Roger was a huge boy. What he lacked in height, he made up for in blubber and bulk. I was kneeling down to build a snowman when his hands pushed my head under until I was submerged in the snow. I felt his hands on top of my head pushing me in more.

It hurt my neck. I can't remember feeling anything but adrenaline when I shot up ripping his hands off me. I looked at him. I was mute. I ran home. I never told a soul. I never remembered it—until that day in class, when the course instructor asked if we'd ever been abused.

Then all the years of him suddenly became tangible. I can hear his putrid nasal voice through his flaring nostrils. I can see him as he fell backwards with his mouth open in surprise, as I twisted free from his grasp. I can feel him standing over me and in front of my bicycle; all those times he blocked me from riding. I can see him waiting for me.

Leslie would come to defend me. She'd be winning until he got hold of her hair. That was the downfall. You couldn't have long hair and win.

In my nightmares I was always racing from the killer. Sometimes I felt myself freeze in my dream. Sometimes I froze when I was awake. I'd slowly turn around expecting someone to crush me, but no one was there.

I began to walk with a hop and threw punches where no threat existed. I began to avoid the 'muggables,' people who appeared weak. I suppose I still do.

If Judy was around I felt completely safe.

An enormous German Shepherd with the light tan face and sweet black dimples on each cheek. Judy was mine. She took up most of my bed but I wouldn't go to sleep without her.

One day, Judy was barking furiously by the front door. I never checked to see what she was barking at. No one did. She got quiet when my dad walked into the house with his undershirt ripped into shreds, his outer shirt gone. We forgot he went up the block to stop the bully, from not letting me ride my bike.

The boy's uncle came out and began hitting my dad, while another male held my dad's hands behind his back. The mother enjoyed herself scratching and clawing at him.

Judy saw everything from our front door, along with the entire neighborhood. No one came to get us. No one helped my dad.

I lived with guilt most of my life for not letting Judy out to rescue my father. It wasn't until many years later that I realized how grateful I was that I *hadn't* let her out. They would have ordered euthanasia, as she would have attacked the people hurting my father.

I still hear her nails scraping the floor at the vet, frantically trying to jump the fence between us. We had come back from a winter trip to Florida. No one told me we weren't taking Judy—my partner—home. We went back into the car and I panicked:

"Where's Judy?!!"

I didn't get to say goodbye or even ask why we were leaving her. My mom was crying and it stunned me into silence. I never saw my mom cry before.

Judy had developed a pancreatic condition from a previous vet stay. The vet was so alarmed by her size that he tranquilized her the entire time. When she came home she couldn't stop vomiting. When Judy vomited, you had to walk a mile around it. Then she lost all her hair.

The next vet who cured her said her dander grew back differently after the illness. That's when Leslie got sick.

I can always hear the nails.

My nose starts swelling, my mouth turns tight and downward that I didn't run out of the car and grab her.

I will never forgive my family for giving Judy away. Leslie could have taken allergy shots and stopped sleeping in the damp basement. There are no excuses for giving a pet away once they become your family. *E V E R.*

Judy made me feel safe, the way my father no longer could. The way

Bram no longer did.

It was through Judy that I learned what betrayal looked like, though I don't know which piece was the worst of it:

Was it my parents' decision to turn away from her? To disregard her love for us like it didn't matter?

Was it that my father couldn't protect me and then gave away the only one who could? Leaving me alone when self-defense wasn't enough?

Was it that I let them do it? That I didn't do for Judy what she had always done for me?

Disregard. Abandonment. Betrayal. Accepting love and loyalty but not protecting it.

Years later, I asked my mom why she never took me to see her. She said: "I guess I was too upset."

And all these years later I still couldn't express myself because I saw her tears again. ●●

22

....

A STRANGER

I moved back to my folks. But I got another call soon from Bram: "I have a hole in my leg."

"A what?"

"A hole—in my leg."

I came into the city, still in my shoulder harness. We went to Barry Zide, who didn't know what a flesh-eating staph looked like and sent us to a dermatologist. While we were in the cab, I handed him back his ring and his charge cards.

I remembered when he gave me charge cards, I just looked at him questioningly.

"Just take them—buy some food," he had a huge grin. I never used them.

I had just gotten the ring back from the designer—he opened the jewelry box:

"It's beautiful. I want you to have it."

He handed it back to me along with the cards: "Just hang on to them. I have no place to put them right now."

After five hours of riding around to different doctors, we went to the ER. People looked at Bram strangely. The consensus was Bram was nuts. This was the first time I saw how the real world viewed Bram, because up until now everyone treated him as royalty. It didn't occur to me that his wealth and status insulated him. He'd have to go under-cover to find any real friends.

I went to the hospital every day. He changed back to the Bram I knew. He drew cartoons on the scheduling board.

I was afraid of giving the staph to my mom and my immunocom-promised patients, and he took my physical distance as rejection. He didn't realize how much I missed him. He couldn't tell how glad I was to be there.

He said: "I'll never forget you helping me. My parents are upset I went with you instead of to their hospital—maybe we can take another trip after this. Please stay with me here. But I know you're not attracted to me anymore."

I watched him conduct business with his hand on his hip—in full con-trol like the commander he was—hearing him grow frustrated with the accountant: "Pects is worried about thousands when I'm talking about millions—there's always a pause—he always has to pause if I want to focus on the more important things instead of wasting time— he doesn't get it."

Bram didn't get it. It wasn't about what *was* important; it was envy. Pects needed to pause because he was the one-down.

Bram was that good.

After four days he convinced the staff to let him go, even though he was still very ill. I picked him up in a downpour and we drove to the apartment.

His kids were coming back from camp and Sally was bringing them to see Bram for his birthday. I wasn't invited to our own apartment. He said he'd spend the following night with me.

I had just ordered a customized cake from Eli's. We argued. His anger unleashed into: "You're a fuckin' asshole, *A FUCKIN' ASSHOLE!*"

I stared in shock and mummied into another room. No man ever spoke to me that way. The only person to ever curse that way was Leslie.

In a few days, I got apologetic calls: "I only cursed because you said you were leaving. You said it like never before, like you really meant it."

"I said I was leaving, *because* you cursed."

"Nancy, come on, you know you said you were leaving before I cursed."

After a couple of weeks he texted me a terrible dream: "We were in a bar and you were laughing at me. Then you left the bar with two men. When I woke up I felt my eyes were wet—I'd been crying. *Please see me!*"

I held out. I even held out when he texted a week later:

"I'm going back to the ER—I think I have bugs in my arm. I feel so disgusting."

Then he called from the ER and I heard a nurse yelling at him over the phone. She was terribly abusive and I heard Bram apologize to her like a scolded little boy. The ER head doc got on the phone when I called and started screaming at me: "Do you know what we're dealing with here? I had to give him a tranquilizer to calm down. I called psych to admit him."

Then Bram texted: "Can they lock you up against your will?"

I got dressed, ready to relive my father's ordeal, only to get another text: "They let me go—the psych people came down and said I was fine."

I looked up the ER doc on the internet. He specialized in alcoholism and addiction.

Three weeks later I got a frantic call in my office: "Nancy, *my eyes… I can't open my eyes!!! Can you please help me?*"

When I entered the apartment he was hunched over a chair with his chin on his chest, eyes closed. I gently opened his eyes to see slits of fluorescent red with a thick watery discharge. I brought an assortment of drops, ointments, and anti-inflammatories—hoping he didn't ulcerate.

"I've never been this depressed in my entire life. Is there any way we can work this out?" he said, as he held my arm to his chest after wincing from all the drops I used.

In another couple of weeks, my Manet was diagnosed with sinus cancer. Dr. Shen didn't even biopsy. He refused to do anything invasive unless necessary. I'd find out too late his noninvasiveness would one day miss an operable cancer in Princy.

Would I be able to sleep without Manet, now that he had trained me?

In an effort to cheer me up, my friend Phil suggested a swim. So we went to the apartment when we knew Bram wasn't there. We scrubbed every inch with disinfectant. We had a great swim and returned to ruined areas of the bamboo floor, wrecked by the rubbing alcohol we had used.

A straw appeared from under the washing machine. It had white powder on it. Next to the machine, Bram's open leather bag had another straw sticking out of it. Inside were two huge glass bottles filled with some kind of substance. Phil ran out to get floor polish.

Later, on our way out, a hunched over man wearing a baseball cap and carrying several large bags rolled into the elevator. He slowly turned to me.

"You make a nice couple," he said angrily, as if the asexual beanpole was my boyfriend.

Phil and I scuttled away as I heard him ask me to come up. Bram was at his best—the nasty side was full-out.

I cried in the doorway of our apartment: *"Why?"*

I wish I could be more like the women who don't cry. Tiger's ex said it's a defect—her inability to show emotion. Why couldn't I be more like them?

Or just stay away—from the men they belong with. ●●

23

....

TURN AROUND

Two months passed. Bram texted me to call him immediately: "My mom passed away. You're the first person I'm calling. Please come."

Do people say *"Go Fuck Yourself"* when a parent dies?

I had nothing to wear, especially to a funeral. I went to a neighborhood shop and the owner spent an hour trying things on me. I told him I wanted no attention—I wanted to fade in with the crowd.

"**NO**—Have a presence. *Wear this!*"

Getting advice from a garment center guy after 15 years of therapy was pretty regressive.

I went to the funeral. The receiving line was a mile long. I passed everyone and told Pects to take me to Bram. I had met his kids only once, yet I wound up in-between Bram and his son, shaking hands with people offering me their condolences.

There was an enormous and endless semi-circular line of people coming toward us. Bram never left my side. I tried to act appropriately; like a grieving woman should.

Leslie had given me her usual unbidden, but sage advice: "Nancy, you don't have to get upset—you have to be strong for Bram; keep a distance."

I went over to his father who was wearing sunglasses to hide his tears: "Try to get him not to do any substance," as he furiously grabbed my hand.

How I wanted to say: "Please, yes, let's talk. I need your help."

How could we get into a conversation about his son's drugs at his wife's funeral?

Bram emailed me after: "I can't begin to tell you how important your support was today and how awful it would have been without you. Please forgive me for my selfishness. Never for a moment am I not aware of you. I love you and need you—always."

Bram only wanted to be with me now. And he wanted me to be only with him. He would fight with me, asking why I had to work so late instead of spending more time with him, while I wondered why we didn't have a home so the office cats could live in one. He became angry when I spent any time with T, who was living at my folks.

He even said: "Leslie has to find her own life," when I mentioned she needed company.

We were going to meet his father and siblings for Thanksgiving in the city. I still hoped for time with his family. I wanted to bring Bram back to them. We never made it.

Two days before Thanksgiving, Bram took a catastrophic fall right outside the hotel. He slashed his forehead, broke his pinky, and fractured his nose in multiple places. It was 11:00 p.m. and raining hard when he called.

Leslie was worried: "You're not driving into the city in this rain Nan— go in the morning, okay?"

My real concern was getting into a fight with him. I had just gotten home from working 12 hours and couldn't handle his moods. I left at 7:00 a.m. and picked him up from the hospital at 8:00 a.m.

But I didn't show the night before. It became something he would resort to over and over. This hit me worst of all.

His face was too broken up to see his family and I was too broken up inside from him. All I wanted was California Pizza Kitchen and to lie down at my apartment. But the hotel gave him their penthouse triplex for the weekend.

There was an isolated elevator to get to the penthouse and then another mini elevator within the triplex to go between floors. There was also a hidden separate area that only could be reached by this mini elevator — there were no stairs to this man cave, which meant you were trapped if the elevator broke down.

The triplex was so private that when I forgot my key, Bram never heard me knocking on any of the doors to get back in. It was so elusive that when I called the bellhop from the hallway, no one even knew where I was.

I went back to our regular suite many floors below. About an hour later the phone rang. He apologized and came to get me.

In the middle of the night I awoke alone. I took a chance and rode up to the man cave. Bram was hunched over doing something on his computer, sitting on the floor.

Another couple of weeks passed and he kissed me one morning:

"Are you on coke?"

"No, why?"

"My lips feel numb."

"Maybe it's the alcohol from cleaning my wounds." He wasn't hyper at all.

It happened another time too. I asked Morda if it could be coke. But Morda was going crazy from phone hang-ups. A woman would call asking for me and hang up. Bram's ex again. Every time he and I got back together, the calls would start.

In mid-December we moved into a different hotel until we could find a real home. The day we viewed the place, a woman came into the elevator. She was in her early twenties. She had bright red lipstick, false eyelashes and coats of makeup. She glared at Bram and didn't take her eyes off of him, smiling the whole time wistfully, as if she were lonely.

I wish we never went back. She was a call girl. ●●

24

....

THE KICK

Soon it was February. My mom had been in the hospital with pneumonia since New Year's. I hadn't seen Bram for most of it and he didn't take a ride to me.

Everyone was watching the Super Bowl, even Morda tuned in. But I couldn't turn on the TV—Bram always had front row seats so people saw him on television. It didn't occur to me he was home having a great night making crystals with his daughter—until he sent me an email saying how special it was.

Sally came home screaming drunk from a football party and kicked him in his spine while his back was turned—in front of their daughter.

Bram sent me a copy of his email to Sally. He told her how sore his back was. Then he sent me her email, which said: "I'll kick your ass again if you don't watch out."

She didn't answer his questions. Instead she ridiculed him for growing up rich, again saying that he never had a real job.

I realized the violent intimacy he shared with Sally had a bigger payoff than life with me.

Another month went by. One evening while billing late at the office I jumped when the phone rang. *Who'd be calling my office at 9:00 p.m.?*

I picked up after 30 minutes of nonstop rings: "Hi—can you let me in? I've been standing outside for half an hour without a coat." It was 10 degrees outside.

I insisted on giving him an eye exam first—to get some emotional distance. It got so late I wanted to go home, but when he put his arms around me it felt like a missing part was returned.

I had two beds in the back—for my late nights and for my cats. Bram and I chose the single bed, instead of disturbing the cats on the queen size. He cradled me for a long time. We both pretended we weren't scared before we made love for the next three hours.

At the romantic conclusion to the hottest, warmest, most right-on sex ever, he said: "Maybe you should freeze your eggs, just in case."

He tried to repair it, saying: "I meant if it didn't work for us naturally, then we'd always have the frozen ones to fall back on."

He was petrified of losing me but I knew he wasn't going to do anything for us. All my insecurities were on high alert.

The drugs were his life now.

I had a sinking feeling it was going to get worse. ●●

25

....

DEANNA

My parents got a call. It had to have been almost two years since they'd heard from Dreck. He wanted money to keep Deanna at home, instead of bringing her to the hospice. I couldn't imagine her kids living with a mother who looked so frightening. I worried about the permanent scars they'd have.

I didn't want to hear Dreck's voice, so I sent him an email saying that I would be glad to give him money, if he would let Deanna rest with Grandma Lily and honor my parents.

He deleted my email unread. I was enraged. Dreck called my office. I screamed: "You killed my sister! How could you never let my parents say goodbye to their own daughter?"

He whimpered on the phone and my hatred grew even more.

I told my parents not to tell me another thing and they honored my request. So I never knew he eventually put her in a hospice. I don't know if my parents knew either. They were afraid to talk to me.

In November, my mother was more distraught over a piece of mail than any outburst I might have. She showed it to me:

Deanna is nearing the end and may not make it to her birthday.

Her birthday was November 30th.

The letter was addressed to no one, with no return address. It was typed in small black print like those serial killer messages you see in the movies. I assumed it was Dreck. Who else would be capable of something so sociopathic?

I was at work when the news came. I had been waiting for it. There had been other times when my dad looked at me and said: *"Bad news."*

My response was always: "Deanna?"

He'd say: "No, my car insurance was canceled," or "Leslie got into another accident," or "We really need you to move out and take the cats with you."

This time I wasn't prepared.

She passed away. It was December 3rd.

My father started heaving over his desk. He didn't show any emotion for two years. He died again that day.

I called Bram. No answer. I called Nathan.

I could fall apart with Nathan, and he'd tell me I was the strongest person he knew. I had to bribe him with $700 to drive me upstate at 3:00 a.m. so we'd make it to the funeral by 8:00 a.m.

My mother had that look I don't like to see. She had called Dreck's mother to get the name of the cemetery.

The witch had said: "Where have you been? Don't you care?"

I answered for my mother: "My mother isn't well. Deanna's tumor was operable...she was supposed to live..." She unleashed a deafening screech like a hyena. Her high-pitched screech was so loud and long...it was chilling. *And then I realized who Dreck inherited his sociopathy from.*

After hearing the voice Deanna hated, I felt worse. My sister's final suffering included that thing for a mother-in-law. That call changed everything. It reminded me how crazy they were.

I assumed Dreck brainwashed the children against me. I wished they knew their mother would never want them growing up in a place where they said 'heighth' and buttoned cummerbunds backwards. Dreck would carry on this charade for the rest of his life, playing the poor widower. The hospice workers must have thought he was an angel.

I couldn't sleep. I prayed for a sign from Deanna. I always wanted to believe in God, but never could. So I asked Deanna to tell me I was doing the right thing.

At about 2:00 a.m. I got a rush of movement along my head, down to my chest, and back again. It kept repeating in a wave lasting 10 minutes. I didn't know if I was hallucinating or if it was her spirit. I felt bliss.

My confidence returned.

I wish Deanna would come visit me again—anytime, anywhere.

We made it to the temple in record time and got there before everyone, including Deanna. When she arrived, the temple was still closed.

Nathan is the kind who says all the right things and shuts up most of the time. A special breed. He didn't question anything I needed to do or tell me to do it differently. He didn't say a word that my parents and Leslie weren't there. He knew my folks were too distraught to face the people who hurt their daughter. He knew Leslie wouldn't go to a cemetery until she wouldn't be leaving.

I explained to the employees I had to say goodbye to my sister privately and asked them to wait for me at the cemetery. I had half an hour with her in the closed temple. Nathan prayed to some heavies. He asked Abraham to walk with her. He was calling in spirits and some of it was in Hebrew.

No one at the Temple was Jewish. This was Utica. The only Jews wouldn't be talking back.

When we got to her grave, no one put in a shovel of dirt. In Jewish culture, everyone takes a shovel and covers the casket, returning them to the earth. Out of the blue, Nathan reeled: *"They're rats,"* and ran to cover her.

We said more prayers.

I stayed until the employees wanted to get on with it. I didn't want to leave her alone. Now I understood why people buried their loved ones on their own land in olden times. I was scared the plot wasn't deep enough. I had recently been to another funeral, in which the grave was so much deeper—too deep for them to come back. But Deanna was so high, I could touch the casket if I wanted to.

It seemed like they didn't mind if she washed away in a rainstorm. Nathan also thought it looked shallow.

I couldn't stop thinking about this and still do. ●●

26

....

T

Bram called me back three days after Deanna's funeral. By then I couldn't talk. I clung to T. In the days since we lost Deanna, she started collapsing.

She was going to be 19 years old on March 29th. I took her to Dr. Shen. He felt her abdomen. She had pancreatic cancer. He didn't need a biopsy. I knew what the end-stage suffering of that was going to be. I thought of Judy and her pancreatic disease. I had thought I'd have a real child to replace T but the unimaginable day was now here.

I awoke and went to sleep with her since I was 26.

Every time I showered, she'd cry when I stayed in too long. When I combed my hair, she brushed her head with her own little brush I propped up against the wall. I taught her to kiss when she was five weeks old. She would only kiss if I used Aquafresh—so I'd been using nothing else for 19 years. She kissed me no less than 10 times a day.

She smelled better than any perfume. She was so elegant, she could walk around anything and never tip it over. But if I didn't wake up for her breakfast, she would paw things onto my head. Eventually I had to re-move everything off the shelf above my head, or it would wind up on me.

One day she started meowing and jumping high off the ground to-ward a light switch. When we took the plate off, it was sparking and a wire was shorted. She got vanilla ice cream for that one—her favorite treat, aside from mayo.

On December 26th, she seemed to be in so much pain; I gave her one of Dr. Shen's tranquilizers. She stretched out on the bed and couldn't move.

It took 24 hours to wear off. For the next two days she'd let me know and I would carry her to the bathroom.

On her final day, Nathan drove me to Shen. She left us and we drove home. Dec 29th. Exactly three months before her nineteenth birthday.

I heard a cry in the backseat of the car as we drove. I've been told you never lose a pet—that they come back to you.

Bram called December 28th, the night before she passed. He invited me to go to Florida the next day for New Year's. He said this *after* I told him where I was taking T the next day.

I was falling asleep one night a few weeks later, and just about to go under—that dreamy time when everything makes sense. I was thinking about names. How nice to have a kid named Bo. But I wouldn't do that to my kid. Also Tru. But I wouldn't make my kid go through life like that either. Use 'em for pets—Tru, Bo—yes, the names I'd give my next cat.

Then there were the names for the child Bram and I weren't having: Ava—I wanted a boy though—Oliver, Evan, Tru, Bo. It all made sense at 3:00 a.m.

The very next day Bram texted that his sister Alexa gave birth to her third child. His name was... Truman Beau.

When I called and told him about my 3:00 a.m. dream, he said:

"That's *wild*. You know Nancy, Alexa said if she ever has another kid, she's going to adopt. You can adopt." ●●

27

....

RED CAMARO

My folks were crashing after Deanna. My mother wet the bed so many times she was in diapers. My father relapsed to his infant state. He screamed weird noises and would shake his feet. He repeated questions not even a child would ask.

Just a few months prior he was fully functioning and examining patients. Smiles were never to appear on his face again.

I wore earplugs to drown out his crazy voice.

I wore earplugs 24/7. I wore them out the door and put them back in when I got home. Little yellow Styrofoam squishes dotted the steps leading to our house, as they were constantly falling out of my pockets. He'd come at me with nonsense questions. I threw paper towel rolls to push him back.

He wouldn't stop. He'd yell when I was in the bathroom, in the bedroom, or anywhere he could find me. I couldn't get away from him, so a locksmith put a lock on my bedroom door. At least I could shut him out, but that meant shutting my cats out too. So I put an extra litter box and water bowls in my room at night.

I started screaming back. But when you're wearing plugs it distorts the volume. So I screamed louder.

Who did I inherit my screaming from?

I don't want to blame my mother for this bad trait of mine, but I do. I'm certain if I didn't grow up hearing her constantly scream I wouldn't have adopted it. You emulate the parent you admire more. Still, no one could picture Sandra as a screamer.

When the garage door broke, my father was outside with the repairman. Soon I heard the man screaming at my father's endless questions. The man turned to me and yelled: "How do you stand him?"

Then I realized maybe my mother wasn't a screamer until my father turned her into one. Maybe I was off the hook then too.

Leslie was soon in the hospital again. She had driven to her primary, who called an ambulance. He didn't tell her he was sending her to the mental hospital.

Normally I would call, run, try to save any family member. I didn't this time.

Being responsible started in Kindergarten. I'd tie the other kids' shoelaces, help put their jackets on, and run errands for the teacher.

I became desperately afraid whenever someone in my family became ill. I didn't know I would stop needing them. Nothing changed in myself. I didn't become stronger emotionally or spiritually.

They were just wearing me out.

I wondered what happened to Leslie's car, so I took a ride. A 30-year-old rusted red Camaro. The embarrassment of our home. It had been Deanna's car. Leslie refused to get rid of it, thinking it was worth a fortune.

Now it was locked with bright fluorescent orange tape, the front wheel bolted, and a taped sticker on the driver's window—the kind you can never get off. Someone put an obnoxious card in the door that read 'Hog Space.'

Did I have to solve this too? How was I going to get her car home? *Would it be so bad if that car disappeared?*

When I came home, my father was shouting a terrible thing happened. I thought about Les in the hospital. "Leslie?"

"No—my car insurance has been canceled again."

He and Leslie had five accidents in the past six months. I told him he shouldn't drive anymore. To tell a man not to drive, especially when he's crazy, is hopeless. He'd find new insurance.

My father then had two more accidents. I wondered when I had to take the keys away, thankful I was able to block him in when it snowed.

He didn't know what temperature to keep the A/C on for the summer—he was truly gone.

Leslie's new pattern *was* the hospital. She kept going back. It gave me a chance to make her living situation nicer—maybe she'd feel better. The contractor said he had a three-week backlog.

"You have to come NOW—she'll be home in three weeks."

I renovated her entire bathroom. They got rid of the mold. I got her a new bed with a frame. Finally, after 15 years, she could get off the floor.

When she returned, she threw the bed out. It was too high. She went back to sleeping on the floor, curled up on a 20-year-old mattress with a hole in the middle.

When would I get out of here—would it ever happen? Real estate seemed to turn a permanent corner at four to six times a property's worth. The mania of NYC real estate was a very real psychological illness. As if a massive collective ego decided their portfolios must remain illogically high, without any correlation to its inherent worth. No one was budging.

I went to see an apartment I couldn't afford, in a building I loved. It was a little over $750K for a place that wouldn't fit half my stuff.

Bram had just thrown away $2 million on hotel rooms while we were together, never making a move on securing us a real home. Now I was priced out of the city. I was becoming seriously depressed.

Living in a mausoleum wears off on you. ●●

28

....

CAFFEINE FREE

I was in my office, billing late into the evening, when I was pulled from my work to the phone. I was speaking with Karen. Karen was the only psychic to tell me:

"Oh this guy… this guy's into it deep. *Major drugs.* Nancy, don't you know pot and alcohol are just chasers? This guy's going to go into the light and get kicked back by St. Peter, and if he doesn't become a Born Again, no one would. But, *Nancy,* run for the hills. He's going to do something to devastate you even further."

Then she made a strange guttural noise.

"Nancy, I'm going to say something in spite of myself. There's major karma here… *major karma!* He may have a heart attack, he might get another woman pregnant along the way, but he'll still want to come back to you… on his way up."

Bram resurfaced again. I wondered if he knew it was torture.

He sent an email: "I want to talk about babies. Do you still want a baby?"

I was at a fertility retreat that we had booked together. It was a natural way for older women to conceive through Chinese medicine. They focused on a three-month cycle, to get an egg generated by the new gluten-free ovary producing it. I went alone. I figured at least I could get off caffeine.

When I came back we met for dinner—he took my hand: "If you have a child, I think it should be my child," he said with deep resolution.

I agreed and told him he had to get a physical and drug testing. He said okay after making me promise to do the same. I also insisted on being his proxy, unable to trust anyone around him.

Then he looked sheepishly at me: "I think I can live without you and then I realize I can't. I thought I screwed the whole thing up. Please forgive me."

He asked me to stay the night.

There were two bedrooms. Bram used one as his spare for all his junk, drugs, papers, suitcases, and anything he didn't want me to know about. He'd always go into that room first, and didn't come out of the bathroom for hours.

Few men I knew could go for more than six months without getting laid. It had been 10 months since we were together. I opened my side table by the bed to put some things away.

Condoms. Assorted.

I reached over and opened the other side table. Gold shoes—high heeled, huge, open backed with rhinestones. Worn.

I went into his room. I didn't care.

I opened his side drawers. White powder—tons of it on a snorting tray. I never saw so much powder.

So why weren't his pupils dilated?

Peeking out from the tray was an old letter of mine that he had saved.

I had written: "If you want drugs and destruction, you don't want me."

I went into the other bathroom, trying to gain some time. In a little while he came into our room.

"Did you sleep with anyone while we were apart?" I asked to his turned away eyes.

"No, just some dates, a little kissing…that was it." I opened the drawers.

"She must have wanted you to find that," he said.

I didn't want to know who 'she' was. He continued to deny it.

"What'd she wear home if her shoes are here?"

I couldn't get past how he left everything for me to find. That they had sex in that bed. That the entire staff knew. She saw my pantiliners and hair ties in the bathroom and used my shampoo. I threw him out and had my nightmare.

For the first time in my life, my dream repeated itself within the same dream:

Bram and I were a bottle fused as one. We exploded into a fiery inferno of particles. If that wasn't bad enough, it exploded again. The explosion was huge, enormous, bursting up to the ceiling with zillions of particles and smoke.

My unconscious was shouting: Yes, it's over—you're over—your love has exploded into nothing.

I tried to fight its meaning—to replace it with the obvious sexual interpretation. But as Perlstein always taught me—if it feels right, you don't need to explain it.

I awoke at 4:00 a.m. and quietly unlocked the door. He was sitting in the living room just staring at the floor.

"Did you have a good time?"

"Hell no, she was *disgusting*. I couldn't wait to get rid of her. Nancy, it was almost a year. You refused to see me!" ●●

29

....

THE CHEATERS

Toward the beginning of my father's descent, after his first stay at Franklin General, he started telling Perlstein he fucked everyone. He fucked his secretary. He had sex with tons of women and there were so many women everywhere. This was the lowest point of his insanity; only part of it was true.

My family was built around my parents' love. I feared for my mother and never saw my father as a ladies man, in spite of his deep blue eyes and thoroughbred legs. Yet I knew my father was guilty. He would never act that way unless there was a reason.

On one of his quieter days, while my mother was out of the room, I asked: "Did you have sex with another woman?"

"Once."

"Did you have a good time?"

"God no…it was the worst day of my life."

He told me her name and where it happened.

Perlstein assured me it was his fantasy. But my father would never lie to me, even if he was crazy. Perlstein *had* to lie to me, to protect my father's patient rights. My dad was more upset than anyone else. It made him sick.

Clinton told the truth: "Because I could." The men who couldn't either had erectile dysfunction or germ phobia.

Why couldn't we have a society like *Lysistrata*, where women banded together and knew they were just as likely to be cheated on by anyone they cheated with.

Someone once called me holier-than-thou for *not* cheating.

Women who go with married men all have the same sickness—they were never loved by their father—a father they could admire. This was usually combined with a dominating, neurotic mother. Dad either cheated or shriveled into some kind of dolt. He never stood up.

I don't blame women who were lied to or were told the man was in an *open* marriage. Although 'open' is still married and leaves question as to why a woman would risk this type of schmuck. But not in France.

The true female manipulators are vindictive over a love they never got as a child. They need to hurt other women. Their value system is wired differently. They're in the power position of their warped fantasy. But not in France.

The other type of female who goes with a married guy is the sweet cheater. This type is rare. These women don't have a bad bone in their body. What they have is self-esteem so diluted, it's in the gaseous state, so you'd have to mix it with some kind of solvent to find any.

The men who cheated because the wife *was* a bitch, get turned on by dominating women, so they married them. But they couldn't live like that, so they sought affairs trying to fill the void they purposely kept empty.

Yet I can't blame a man who's in a lonely marriage with a bitchy wife. If this man left, he'd give his kids some self-esteem, but inertia sets in and he'll do anything to breathe. Their daughters pay the price their wives never do.

There's no pill for character.

Now cheating is a disease so insurance can pay for your luxe getaway, where you'll be massaged, soothed, and everyone will ask if you're okay. *Take me please.* You'll have sex with all the other addicts when the meeting's over. Just like heroin—cheating is life-threatening and the idiot can't stop.

The shrinks are making this up as they go along. Poor character has its own ICD-10 code.

Maybe he's incapable of lasting romantic love never having seen it. There's not much to admire in women except their vaginas and they keeping picking women who prove it. It's hard to get healthy when you're surrounded by liars and hypocrites. It's impossible if you're rich.

There's a small percentage of women who want the cheater to stay to keep him miserable. They want their husbands to pay for what their absentee fathers did.

The men who take it had mothers who weren't there either. Who's paying for this fantasy? The kids they're *protecting*.

The real freaks are the couples who are 'in love' because it screwed somebody else over. These unions last. Their love is always at the expense of someone else. If that someone else weren't there, their love wouldn't be either.

Was my dad one of them? Was Bram?

Is it cheating if the cheater hates the actual experience and wishes it never happened? He doesn't care he got away with it, he never had fun doing it.

The cheating is done—the betrayal is real.

One of my parents' friends would say he was going to the movies; another would just take the elevator to a neighbor when his wife was at work; and yet another took off his ring whenever he traveled.

It's hard finding my true love—someone with a healthy libido who's loyal like me.

My mother always says sex is the most important thing in a relationship. She says: "If you respect each other, but the sex is bad, how happy can you be? But if the sex is great... at least you're having great sex."

I don't want love without passion. And I can't feel passion without love.

I can orgaz without either, but that's boring. I'd be afraid to meet someone who could orgaz more than myself. I couldn't keep up with two of me. That would mean double sweat, double time, and more laundry. At least when I did that, I was alone. Being alone can be brutal.

But that's why there's *variable speed* control. ●●

30

....

PINHEAD

We went to my primary, because now I *had* to find out if he had anything. I privately asked him to test Bram for every drug, and everything he could get enough blood for. I told him to forget HIPAA, because this was a person's life at stake.

I asked him if Bram looked funny.

After both our blood tests, he asked Bram if I could come in. Bram said no. But the pinhead called out: "Nancy… come in here."

I sat down, extremely angry Bram hadn't wanted me there. "I don't know what that is on his arms, but I need to rule out leprosy. He must get tested for this," Pinhead said.

Then we went into a bank, and Bram notarized me as his proxy. On the ride back to the city, he switched from fuming to smiling in a matter of minutes: "Thanks for making me do that… I really love you. I think it's time I put you in my will."

Pinhead finally sent the blood work saying everything was okay. He never tested for drugs, as I had asked. But when I showed the results to my cardiologist, he said Bram was imminently at risk for diabetes, cardiac arrest, and clot formation. He wanted to know if Bram had flown recently. But he refused to see Bram without a vascular surgeon's opinion and blood cultures.

When I finally got hold of a vascular surgeon after hours of calls, he refused to see Bram without a report from the cardiologist.

The day we went to get the cultures Bram said he'd do anything not to go and once we got there he kept begging to leave. We sat in the cafeteria, reading a magazine together. It felt so odd and wonderful—just to sit and talk. We hadn't for so long.

I asked the nurse if he looked funny after she took some blood from his arm. When he got the leg Doppler and the technician passed along his swollen calves, no eyebrow was raised. I was looking at her.

Please, someone, say he looks frightening.

I spent two more days tracking down another vascular guy, but he wouldn't see Bram until an infectious disease doc took a look. I called the cardiologist, telling him I got nowhere. He hung up.

The entire time I wondered why no one saw what I was seeing. Every single MD negated the look I saw in Bram's eyes. Not a single one suspected drugs.

We went to my dermatologist, but he said Bram had: "Delusional Parasitosis." ●-●

31

....

TRADER JOE'S

Another month went by. I was sleeping in my office now. Rosa, my angel, was leaving for Mexico. This was always a disaster.

Rosa couldn't speak English, was 4'8", and round as a tomato. Like an ant, she could lift far more than her own weight. She gave insulin to my cats twice a day. I asked Bram if I could move two cats to the hotel.

He said: "Bring 'em all."

There it was again: Hope. How could he *not* be the right guy? I was mercilessly ridiculed by men about my cats. Bram had rescued a feral cat and invited him into his home.

I moved in and didn't see Bram. He went on a *real* business trip to Vegas. I was grateful to have a place for my cats. But I got a frantic call from my father as soon as I got there.

He found out where I was from Caller ID. I had to hide from him now as he was uncontrollable.

"Nancy, Mommy and Leslie are in the hospital."

"What do you mean? *Both* of them?"

"Just what I said—Mommy went in this morning and Leslie went in tonight." He began to cry.

My mother had fallen again. I didn't know what was wrong with Leslie. Next my mother began calling no less than 20 times a day. She was dialing nonstop. They had taken away her Verapamil.

The MD took her off her meds, to try to figure out why she kept falling. I asked if it occurred to him that since she had MS, maybe that's *why* she kept falling, since that's what MS people do and that if he didn't want her to die, maybe he ought to give her back her Verapamil.

Somehow I managed going to work, getting back to do the insulin, and riding to the hospital to see my mom. I only survived because of Bram. Bram told me to use his car service for anything. The car service saved me.

He kept offering to buy me a car: "Come on, go pick one out today."

I couldn't let Bram think I needed money. I couldn't tell him how bad my financial situation had become. I started saving every penny. Cereal lasted even longer than the Trader Joe's Trek Mix I had been subsisting on.

Upon Bram's return he fell in love with Princy. They had the exact same hair color. The cats made the hotel feel more like a home. It was a happier place. But Bram was still locking himself in the bathroom for hours. He would come out when I left. He never told me when he would arrive or planned to leave. Except for our doctor visits, we never saw each other. I couldn't have sex with him, because I felt no love from him.

One day Bram came to find me. He was starting to look green and his eyes were dark: "Do you think you could get this tested for parasites?"

He gave me some skin samples from scratching his arms—and feces.

I gave them to Bubbles, an ophthalmologist friend, but he didn't know what to test for. It was awkward. I was risking my reputation, but Bram was more important.

Bubbles said: "Common things happen commonly. Uncommon things happen uncommonly. And it is more common to have an uncommon presentation of a common disease, than to have a common presentation of an uncommon disease."

The next day Bram laid a microscope slide on the table, showing me what came out of the sores on his arms. A microscope—maybe he bought it from Hammacher Schlemmer. I was jealous of the scope because once I saw it, I knew Bram was lost to me. He wasn't looking at anything having to do with us—there was no 'us.'

I looked in the scope and saw a few long skinny things, which... *moved*.

I called a friend who was head of the pathology lab at a NYC hospital. I ran over with the slide, but she couldn't see anything on it to test. I pointed out the tiny glob on the broken end and she asked me what we should test for. She and the pathology resident thought it over.

Certain substances would dilute the glob and others wouldn't highlight it enough. I suggested putting it under the scope to take a look. The resident was intrigued. I was grateful they didn't send me away.

The first time she put the slide on the scope, the slide jumped up and fell off. We all laughed.

The next time she put the slide on, it did exactly the same thing.

The third time the resident ran into the corner with a cross sign in front of her face, screaming the slide was possessed. I took a picture of the frightened resident because at least this was entertaining.

Finally she got the slide on and held onto it. They hooked it up to a projector and showed it to me magnified a zillion times.

Clothing fibers.

I asked them why it moved.

They said: "Things move; air moves it."

But when I told Bram his 'parasites' were clothing fibers… he emailed me articles of more people who *also* had 'parasites.' ●●

32

....

MAIDS, PSYCHICS, AND SCHIZOS

A minor problem arose—which turned into the thing that would test our relationship like nothing else. The housekeeping manager called the room:

"Your cats are soiling our nice towels."

"My cats never soiled any towel."

"I'd like to bring up some rugs right now, if that's okay."

"No—it's not okay, I'm rushing to work. Please don't call again."

She called again the following morning and repeatedly called every day hence.

Much to my chagrin, I had become dependent on a psychic when T was passing. She kept calling and said: "I'll help you get through this."

I couldn't believe how much she cared about my cat.

She got me at that perfect time—I was losing my man and my feline child. It was now several months later when she told me how much Bram loved me. She kept asking to meet him. Finally I relented, thinking maybe he'd be intrigued and come out of the bathroom.

After bringing him to half a dozen MDs with zero results, I had nothing to lose.

She was either schizophrenic or inherently evil, I would find out too late.

When Bram gave her his card, I cringed. He even kissed her hand. I never thought he would do that.

She was almost 6 feet, and half of her 250 pounds hung from amazon-like sausage arms. She had once told me she could just sit on someone if they were bothering her.

Bram wouldn't understand my doubts of someone I introduced him to. I avoided telling people who Bram was. People viewed me differently—their entire body language changed. I didn't like their sickening reactions.

Now she had his card and his address.

Soon she became overbearing—finally securing her retirement fund: Bram. She started meditations with him and went into past lives. She had something called *Peyote* and said we should all do it together. I didn't know what it was—she said it would help him realize his past life where he was trapped in a basement in the Holocaust.

When she came over, it was the only time he *wasn't* in the bathroom. I left the room during these sessions, and wondered what I got myself in to. The last time she came over, I paced the hotel basement, with horrible thoughts when it ran past three hours. I wound up in the hospital the next day with my first asthma attack in several years.

The psychic told me the towels were an excuse. She said the housekeeper was in love with Bram.

I wasn't the insecure type usually. I knew when a man loved me. I knew Bram's love had begun to change by the hour, or rather which drug he did during which hour. I also knew he feared losing me forever no matter how much distance he craved. I knew the psychic was trying to manipulate me. I knew the hotel staff knew more about his secret life than I did.

But to have people you'd never allow into your life know things you don't—is unbearable. To be insecure about a housekeeper, who had always struck me as plain and country, gave me new nightmares.

I imagined all women were after Bram and that he flirted back with them. This was a new low for me. Part of it was true unfortunately. Both the part about women wanting a rich man, and the part about Bram wanting to please them.

I didn't realize Bram was this type of man until I saw it at another hospital stay.

He smiled at a nurse with a kind of smile: "Hope you'll be nice to me and like me … *so I'm going to flirt with you.*"

I didn't want to bother Bram about the towel nonsense, when his father and brother were antagonizing him. He had his mother's unveiling coming up. He asked me three times to go. I knew I'd be standing alone, not amongst friends and who knew if he'd show up.

And Bram would blame me for not getting to know his kids at an unveiling. I couldn't stomach the massive stone they commissioned for their mother either. I had buried Deanna only five months before in the sorriest way.

Then Bram told me his father was getting married again, while we were no longer engaged. I wondered if his father would show up at his wife's unveiling with his fiancée.

That next week the city had its first hot day before summertime. The hotel refused to turn on the A/C. Low blood pressure got me and I needed a lighter shirt. I went into the walk-in closet and the door quietly closed—by itself.

A terrible thought flashed through my mind before I was cognizant of it. The closet opened inward—you had to push it in from the outside or pull it from the inside. It was a *magnetic* closure.

There was no handle on the inside.

I thought of closets at home and at work, not accepting this profound negligence—they all had handles inside...how was this happening?

There was no ventilation. It felt 100 degrees hotter inside. It was dark. I was in my underwear. I had no cell.

I didn't know when Bram would come, and if he did, he wouldn't check the closet. Samson and Princy scratched and cried on the other side. I was glad they were free. Feverish thoughts came. It was just too hot.

I thought of Michele Lee from 20 years ago in *Knots Landing*, when she's trapped in a burning house. She was pulling wood out of the nails—time closing in.

I thought of the little boys who had suffocated in a car trunk. How could they make trunks without safety handles inside?

I thought of a stock broker I had worked with years back. He was in Vietnam and breathed air through a straw for two hours hiding in a swamp, while his entire outfit was killed.

I wondered if I could lie with my head near the bottom of the door and suck in air. I thought of all these things instantly, all at once. I had to be in *The Survivors Club*.

I reached down to the floor and tried pulling the door open with my fingers, but it was barely five millimeters off the ground and such thick wood, my fingers became raw and bloody as I tried to get under it. The hotel hangers were those thick wooden ones. Everything was high-end, thick, and useless.

I grabbed the metal top off the hanger, pulled it out and tried hooking it under the door. But it was too strong and thick, and the top broke in two, neither piece being long enough for leverage. I could barely see.

I grabbed one of the hangers I had brought from home. A thin wire one. I shaped it into a curved triangle and bent both ends up and carefully hooked it around the corner of the door. It fit outside!

The first couple of yanks, only pulled the hanger back to me. The magnetic closure was too strong and the diameter of the bottom door too wide and the wire too thin for power. I had to hurry before I passed out.

I made the curve steeper, fitting it back under again, and like Sigourney Weaver in *Aliens*, whispered "lucky, lucky, lucky, lucky," and yanked with all my might as quickly as I could. It popped open! I crawled to my cats. *(If not for that thin wire hanger from home.)*

Bram arrived days later. He went into the closet, shut the door and stood there. A couple of minutes later he slammed his hand against the door a few times. It popped open. He told me to try. I couldn't do it. Then he told me to hit my hip against a certain location. It popped open.

I had a nightmare that night: *Someone was chasing me in the stairwell of the hotel. I tried climbing up and then down, because every landing had a door without a handle.*

I awoke as someone was closing in on me.

Figuring I was vulnerable, the psychic told me it was better Bram become intimate with her first, so he could learn intimacy with me.

Uh huh, right.

She told him things about me. He would then ask me things she told me not to tell him. This caused a great divide—coming from me this time.

I confessed to Bram that I sent a letter to the housekeeping manager to leave me alone and signed his name. That the psycho psychic told me to sign his name. She even edited it.

He didn't get mad. He said he didn't want to see her anymore. He hugged me very tightly and said: "She's disgusting and makes stuff up as she goes along."

He kept hugging me. I wondered what happened that last three-hour visit.

I came to the hotel one night after he sent me a romantic text. We got closer after realizing her intentions. When I walked into the spare room he refused to look at me. I noticed a stack of emails on the bed that looked like mine.

They *were* mine—over 50 of them.

Emails I had written to the psycho psychic about Bram. She had highlighted and written notes over them, implicating I was not to be trusted.

I can't stand him, he's never here, he left again when I was ill, his hole-filled brain…

Nothing was worse than what I said to him in person. None of it was even revealing. They were emails of anguish that he was never there.

There was a warm letter, too, but it was from the psychic—with a self-addressed envelope for him to write back to her. A new separate email that *"Nancy doesn't know about,"* and a new phone number. She finished her invitation with: *"Will miss ya"*—that phony thing women who can be *'light'* do—to attract men you can never give an ultimatum to.

He finally yelled: ***"The relationship is over!!! You hate me. I read those emails. You can't stand me."*** He was devastated.

I was surprised by the raw agony in my own voice, as I cried: ***"NO!"*** A sickening feeling swept over me. Not only about her, but *emails?*

I had gold shoes and condoms in my drawer after my return. Had I slept with another man and left boxers in his drawer? I went into our room, with a mini asthma attack.

I jumped into the shower needing relief. In less than five minutes, he opened the shower door and hugged me with his eyes distraught and red. We stood that way for a long time, dripping wet.

I got a text the next day on the ride to my parent's house:

"Don't worry Nan—just a blip in the road. I love you."

But significant damage was done. Those emails made him feel like I went behind his back—he never realized the anguish those emails contained. Instead—his image of me changed.

I made a mistake and trusted someone bad. For him.

After sleeping a few days at the office, I needed a real shower. Bram texted three times that he was in Jersey and wanted to know if I'd be home later. He never cared if I was there and it was never our home.

I ignored him. I was looking forward to a shower I could take in peace—clean sheets, soft bed.

It was nice and quiet when I arrived and I jumped in the shower. I relaxed and decided to get some late night pizza. When I came out of the bedroom at 11:00 p.m., the spare room was open with the TV on.

He caught me off guard by saying hello. *Why wasn't he with his kids?* I didn't respond but hurried out. I didn't know I had rage.

When I returned he said: "Nancy if you're not going to talk to me, you shouldn't stay here."

"Don't worry I'm leaving, why don't you load up?" as I pulled his gallon of Ketel One from the freezer and placed it on his nightstand. Then I saw a condom on the bed.

He grabbed it screaming: "Don't look through my stuff. It's old."

But how old could it be? He was packing for a trip to Florida.

It brought back the gold shoes—the scuffed high heels left in a drawer for me to open. A huge wide foot. It was a big woman.

What did she wear home? Did she sleep over? Did she see my things in the medicine cabinet? Was Bram wearing the shoes himself?

Who was she—someone from his past, someone from the dealer, was there more than one, was it partying, coke, dancing, weird sex? Did Sally want sex? And who would do that? Who would have sex with someone who didn't love them?

Bram's lover only needed drugs and a room for the night. I know most people wouldn't call it cheating since we had been apart for almost a year. He said he'd never be a monk. *But my partner wouldn't want frivolous sex.*

"So you think you're a good father?" I asked as I watched him pack his coke tray.

His face contorted as his hands raised up to block his ears. He took my arms, lifted me up and carried me to the door like a car hydroplaning. Then he lightly pushed my chest and out the door I went. It was smooth, just like him. I saw red fingerprint marks on my arms.

"You're this guy?"

My anger was taking over. Why wasn't his door locked by now—did he want this to continue?

I started walking to his bathroom to get some tissues, but he grabbed my shirt spinning me around. I had to hold on to him not to fall. I didn't realize something was *in* the bathroom, or I would have ran in to see.

We hugged desperately. He cried: "Please don't leave me…I've never loved anyone half as much as you, never needed anyone the way I need you."

"Please please…just tell me what you're using."

He pleaded for me to go into the other room. Then he went into the bathroom.

I climbed onto his closet, which used to be a bed. I pushed aside cereal, clothes, candy, fishing lines, guitar, books, and half-eaten food.

He peeked out of the bathroom shouting: "Don't touch my shit!" Then he made some percolating noises the water couldn't drown out. I heard snorting, sniffing, blowing.

When he came out, he sat on the bed near the light—his eyes had that look again. But it was much worse—he looked psychotic.

I gulped: *"You're going to die…YOU ARE GOING TO DIE."*

All he said was: "If I got us an apartment, I'm afraid you'll blackmail me."

I searched his eyes, his arms, his chest—I feared his staph would return because of all his open wounds.

If I called the hospital, they could hold him for three days. But what if they were like the doctors my father had? If we were married, I would have taken him to Perlstein. I pictured being shut out of his hospital room if he had a stroke. I wasn't family.

No one knew Bram and I were never together. They assumed he was with me. He told his father and brother we were living together and that he was going on the straight and narrow. He told me his father was going around the company asking people if they saw him using drugs; that his brother tried to punch him in the face.

Who was I supposed to trust?

I had no leg to stand on, I wasn't his fiancée anymore.

Bram came into our room at 4:30 a.m. I was awake. I couldn't turn around.

He spooned me for half an hour, thinking I was asleep. But his entire body shook, his legs kicked. I turned my head around as he got up holding a pillow with his head down—defeated.

I wanted to reach out, but I was defeated too. ●●

33

....

IN THE RED

I went back to sleeping at the office.

I kept begging my dad to help. It was too hard popping lenses into frames all day, getting those tiny screws in, bending the frames, dispensing, ordering all the scripts and doing the exams. My thumbs were falling off.

He did all the grunt work, began all the exams, and would wink if it was a difficult case—like the three-year-old who couldn't see her own mother's face. Her pediatrician never took two seconds to use an ophthalmoscope to see the dull reflex. My father and I were the perfect team.

My neck became so stiff—I didn't want to wind up like one of those dentists in a collar. I wondered what giving a blowjob would be like— it had been so long.

First physical and then financial reality set in.

After 14 years of escalating profits, I was down a devastating $100K. When I inquired, Morda showed me the list of days I missed—close to 80, not counting all the days I came late and left early.

I asked her what happened.

Bram.

I had lost so many days running to his latest crisis. I took a look at the prior years—down by 50K in 2008 and even more in 2007.

He always said: "I want to take care of you… you never have to worry again." Now I had lost a fortune because of Bram—the rich man.

How would I explain this to a potential buyer?

Soon after my eyes started shaking. The first time I denied it and hoped it would go away. They shook only in the mornings. After a few weeks, it happened any time of the day. *I had nystagmus?* It had to wait.

I wanted to lease my building to one person—which is called a Triple Net Lease—NNN. They could manage the tenants from hell. Like the young women who stopped paying rent and moved out, while their cousins continued to use the apartment for sex. And the Peeping Tom who kept little dolls in his apartment. He would walk along the fire escape to spy on his former friend's now pregnant girlfriend. The weary teacher who flooded three floors by keeping her rag in the sink. And my favorite—the security guard who drank heavily and kept a small arsenal in his closet. He would shine his flashlight into my office at midnight to check on me.

My father had built two illegal apartments during one of his manic phases. He refused to raise the rent of two elderly women, who paid $450 for their three bedroom apartments (even though they weren't rent controlled). Instead, he built two small apartments to cover expenses.

I had to fix it. I invested every cent of profit to remake the entire building. But my father's compassion was hard to rectify. Each new contractor took my money and never got the building up to code. They knew they had me.

After 10 years of corrupt contractors, one of the elderly tenants had passed on. I threw out everyone else and heated the entire building for

Morda's mom and my cats.

If HealthPlus paid optometrists as much as Medicaid did, (and that's a sad statement) my neck wouldn't be so stiff. But they decided my patients didn't need that extra $15 procedure to rule out an orbital tumor. Somehow that $15 turned into $100 when they paid an ophthalmologist to do it. I did most tests for free. It was better than being sued for not doing them. HealthPlus was finally bought out and I was about to be also.

A few ophthalmologists were interested in buying my practice. I was leaning toward Bubbles but he always smelled. His car smelled even worse. I threw some Downy sheets into his Jaguar—worked like a charm. I noticed his fingernails were filthy, when we met for coffee. He was operating on some of my patients. He blew it off, saying he had been fixing his computer.

He treated his patients with utmost kindness and the women he dated with utmost cruelty. Like the woman who gave him a blowjob on a first date—she had misrepresented herself in her online photo. He deserved something for taking her to dinner.

I asked if he satisfied her too. He said she had her period.

"What about your hand?" I asked.

He grimaced.

A while back Bubbles paid a visit to my new apartment. He started petting my cat Manet. I was wearing shorts and my bare leg was getting some of his caresses. He suddenly jumped up: "Are my pupils dilated? I think I'm having a panic attack," and then ran into my bathroom.

When he came out I shoved a mini little pizza into his mouth, wondering if he was hypoglycemic. His blue eyes bulged: "That tastes good but

I have to get out of here."

He ran out the door, leaving $50,000 in deposits on the bathroom floor.

Two weeks later he told me he's only had a panic attack twice before and that he can't be alone in a room with me. I was flattered and vowed to never let him operate on me.

The next time we spoke, he said out of nowhere: "Nancy, I'm your friend, but this is business. If your practice is a 'shell,' then I would not be willing to purchase it."

"What are you talking about? We've been here since 1898, over 100 years—the oldest practice in NYS, and I have income statements. Why do you always have to insult me?"

"Nancy, you did not listen to me, as usual, so I will repeat it—if your practice turns out to be a shell, if there's even the *possibility* it would turn into a shell…"

I hung up.

Still, at our next meeting he said: "I'll buy your practice for half of what you want, pay you half the rent, and relieve you of the burden. I'll draw up a temporary contract. No worries."

I never heard from him again until he told me: "I don't really need to be on Fifth."

Or was it his partner's wife again?

He said: "I think it's time we had dinner with my partner."

"Is he religious? I can't deal with that."

"No—he's married."

"What, to a *beautiful Asian woman?*"

His eyebrows raised: "Yes, how'd you know? Her name is Carol and she's an optometrist."

"I know her."

"How could you possibly know my partner's wife?"

"What are the chances an Asian optometrist named Carol was dating a Jewish ophthalmologist 10 years ago, and it's *not* her?"

I left out that Carol once told me: "Spanish men are fast as shit and these guys in our school are the ugliest guys I've ever seen." She left out her boyfriend.

"She won't want me in business with her husband. The deal's off."

I didn't hear from him for three weeks. When I did, he said: "You were right. They said it would be 'weird' if we were in practice together."

I met with Bubbles at his office two years later. He still smelled. He took his pen and slashed it across my net income on the financial statement:

"What if it's only half this?"

"That's why you're an asshole."

He looked bewildered.

"How can you say 'What if it's half,' when you're looking at my income statement?"

I couldn't sell my practice to another ophthalmologist who changed his name to lose his Jewish identity. He didn't know one of his young patients had a whopping nystagmus when you occluded one eye, nor did he care when I told him. He was quoted in *The New York Times*, as being an expert in pediatric ophthalmology.

I couldn't sell it to the group whose Manhattan office rent meant their patients had to cover it—so their records were doctored for that laser surgery they never had, or the surgery they had but didn't need, and the glaucoma that didn't exist.

I couldn't sell it to the well-known glaucoma expert that celebrities flock to—the one who went on junkets to Thailand in drag—to meet little boys.

Nor could I sell it to the one-eyed optometrist who came in with his two partner MDs. The older MD was bleeding from his forehead, and the younger MD kept picking his teeth.

Which made me realize why all three of them didn't have their own patients to examine and wanted to buy mine. ●●

34

....

REVELATIONS

The next day Morda came into my exam room with a strange look: "It's Bram."

For a second I wanted to stay where I was—call him back later. But I picked up.

He was quiet, contrite and could barely say hello: "I'm in the hospital. They did an intervention."

"Where? When?"

"Friday morning—would you please come?"

"You want me to visit you there?"

"Yes. Can you come now?"

What if his family saw my letters when they were in the apartment? *Or those pictures?*

I took a cab to the hotel. The staff was nastier than usual. The manager was paranoid after the intervention:

"This has never happened before—that social worker barging upstairs. You haven't been here in a year—I can't let you in without his approval; you're not on the lease anymore."

"But we lived here. I found this place. He wouldn't be here if not for me."

"Doesn't matter," as he brushed me off.

When I asked Bram to call them, he said: "Why do you want to go in there?" Still hiding things from me I realized.

"What if there's stuff they shouldn't see?" I said, starting to feel sick.

He said okay—but I got the feeling I was on the outside.

The place was wiped clean. Every filthy drawer immaculate. The refrigerator spotless. Every inch was hospital sterile. All my things were gone.

I called his brother: "Matt, if you were going to do an intervention, why didn't you do it two years ago?"

"Excuse me?" someone replied in a voice I didn't recognize.

I repeated it and asked if his cell was clear. I repeated his name too. The voice became colder. "This is disgusting; it's been a pleasure," I said as I hung up.

Immediately after, a social worker called from the rehab: "Hi, my name is Ron and Bram gave me your number. I wanted to talk about Bram's condition—what do you know about the carriage house?"

"I only know he's abused and resorts to drinking when he's there."

"Yeah, we've been getting that idea. Is there any physical abuse you know of?"

"I just know his ex drinks and kicked him in his back—when his daughter was there. But he was having a lot of issues at work too—I'm not sure who to trust."

"Yeah—we saw a little bit of that with his father and brother."

"I thought Bram didn't want them there."

"Well, they came and I know you're coming tomorrow. We'd like to do couples counseling with you and Bram. But Bram is very weak, this is going to take a *long* time, and he may need to live in a support group for a while."

I wasn't sure what he meant by 'weak,' since I hadn't seen Bram in months and only knew him to be Hercules, even when he was stoned off his ass.

"Well, I won't be able to do counseling or see Bram if he goes back to living in the carriage house. We can't be a couple then."

"That may actually be the best tactic for him—that may get him to face things," he said.

"Wouldn't it be better for Bram if I disappeared for awhile? Isn't that what they tell people to do—*not* to be involved?"

"Well, the new research says that supportive people help the process and it seems you're the best one for his recovery. I think that might work— if you would tell him you can't see him unless he leaves the carriage house."

When we got off the phone, I felt good for the first time in years. That social worker was smarter than all the MDs I'd wasted time with.

I looked through the apartment once more and gave up, but soon as I got outside: "Nancy?" someone half-shouted. I didn't recognize him. "It's Matt."

Did he fly over?

"What are you doing here?"

"I came over because you said you couldn't get in…"

He looked sweaty, like he ran over, worried there was something he didn't know about. Instead of asking him why he was so mean on the phone, I yelled: "What were you doing? Why'd you wait so long? How come you never called me? *Now* you do this? Where's my stuff?" I was furious.

"What stuff?"

"My stuff—my letters, my stuff. Listen, just take the company, I want Bram alive."

"So you think this was just about the money?"

"Yes. He was bleeding and turning green…how did you just stand there? What made you finally take action?"

"The Taconic crash—all those people were killed. I was afraid he'd get in a car accident. And we lost a business account after they saw what Bram looked like."

"So it's okay if he has a heart attack or stroke…it's only because you were afraid the company would get in trouble and lose money or its reputation," I yelled.

"Nancy, Bram has a disease. He's had emotional issues for years. Why do you think he married his first wife? Let's go sit down somewhere."

"What? What's that got to do with anything? Don't you smoke pot and didn't you drop out of college? Bram isn't the only one with problems in your family."

"Why are you bringing up college?" he asked, looking pissed and embarrassed until a smile crossed his lips: "Aren't all family's dysfunctional?"

The pothead who spelled 'oppinion' three times in a single text began to preach to me: "You're a healer. You know Bram just came back after traveling to the Bahamas with Sally and the kids. You really should break up with him. You deserve better."

I started to feel dizzy. The guy in the 3.4 million dollar townhouse wanted his brother to be without me—I was a threat to the handle they all had on him.

"When Bram missed Iris' unveiling, that really killed me," Matt went on.

"Do you mean your mother? Why are you calling her Iris?"

I said this as a distraction. I needed to absorb how badly he wanted to destroy my connection to Bram. He started getting smaller and smaller too—doing some type of straddling split in the middle of the block until he was a couple of feet shorter than me. This endearingly childish behavior uncloaked the tough guy he was trying to be.

"Were you and Bram engaged?"

"Yes—two days before you kicked me out of the picture."

"Well had we known you were engaged, we wouldn't have done that of course."

"No, that's not it. You have no idea what etiquette is—you don't kick out *any* guest."

"I didn't even know Bram had an apartment in the city, did you?" Matt interjected. "I can't believe he never told me."

"Look Matt, I don't want another person dying on me after losing my sister. And…"

"Nancy, I had no idea your sister died," he interrupted again as he put his hand to his heart. "I can't imagine losing a sibling."

He couldn't decide which role to play.

"*But you almost did!* Bram's blood report indicated he was on the verge of a heart attack. You know Matt, Bram would do anything for you. He'd lie down in the street for you. When I see him tomorrow—" I immediately wished I hadn't told him Bram wanted me to visit.

"*You're going?* He told me he didn't want to see me again." Matt looked into the distance, calculating something—planning.

As I gave him the proxy, he said: "Thanks for giving this to me," holding his sarcasm.

The following morning a peaceful feeling came over me as I approached the rehab. I had no peace since finding out about his trip with Sally.

Bram was sitting with his back to me, wearing a green shirt with some food on it, unkempt hair, reading a magazine. He looked fine—from behind. The same messed up Bram I always knew.

I had this strange feeling as I approached… that the world had changed.

His eyes were watery and sad. We sat outside for a while, getting used to him being real again. Then he showed me his room. We kept the door open, as we grabbed hold of each other.

He cried: *"I screwed up your whole life…I should have given you two kids by now."* He rolled into a ball as he rocked toward me.

I wanted to say: "It's not too late," but I couldn't. I was too shocked because this was the Bram I fell in love with—the man I hadn't seen in so long.

"All my liver functions are normal—there's no damage. You saved my life," as he held me tighter thanking me for getting him to drink less. "My father was here today again and was upset the tests came out normal. Why would he be upset they came out normal?"

"You know he has problems…what do you mean he was here?"

"After you gave Matt the proxy, he and my dad took another ride. Matt said you're an 'enabler.'"

"*ME?*"

Bram continued: "But I said: 'She's not an enabler; she doesn't do any drugs. She's the only one who confronted me and made me go to doctors.' He's mad you told him he's spoiled and should go back to school. No one's ever spoken to him that way. Oh, and look at these. Stallion had everyone write about me for the intervention."

Matt had hired a social worker for the rich and famous, who wanted his own TV show. They were horrible letters written by Bram's family and friends. It was part of Stallion's *therapy*.

These letters were designed to empower everyone except the patient. I had read that interventions could be lethal if the *real* cause was a psychological and chemical imbalance.

The most scathing letter was from his brother-in-law—a man of great importance. He only had a substantial job because Bram promoted him, after his writing career never happened. Finally, someone would read something he wrote.

After slamming Bram every way he could, he included stories that had nothing to do with him—but they helped me. One story told how Bram invited a woman to an event years before but when Bram arrived late—his mother lost respect for the woman, because the woman didn't leave.

I sat back. I finally understood.

As I read the other letters, I began to realize why Bram was so distorted. And why his mother hated women so easily.

Instead of realizing it would have shown poor etiquette for that woman to leave, she hated a woman who reminded her of her own life—her husband's absences, deception, and her own inability to stop it. I wanted to leave right then too.

I wanted to throw up.

What upset me terribly was Bram's sister allowing her husband to write such a letter. I knew she adored Bram. Where was her loyalty to him? Maybe they were too similar—neither one able to confront.

Albert Ellis told me: "Blood is sicker, than water." Now I was seeing what he meant.

I wondered how Bram could ever know love, since his version of love was interlaced with disloyalty.

We took a walk and had some dessert together. We decided I'd come back tomorrow. He was being moved to a more independent building.

When I arrived the next day with Bram's car service, the nurse came out smiling. We had met the prior visit. She called my name and directed us towards Bram. As soon as she said my name, a women entering the building halted and whipped her head around glaring at me. *Sally!*

I knew from all the pictures Bram had inadvertently shown me: "You might get upset, Sally's in this one." He did that a lot.

Early in the relationship he brought over a baseball video of his company's yearly picnic outing. He wanted to show me how he pitched the game.

"Don't worry Nancy, there's no competition. I'm in love with *you*," he said before he hit play. He continued to look at me: "Don't you know *you're the one* I've always been in love with?"

I didn't know why he was saying this—I wasn't jealous. It seemed as if he wanted me to be. I wondered why he continued to bring her into our new relationship. But the video kept rolling and before I could stop him, there she was—up close when his father zoomed the video into her face. I was surprised how plain she looked.

But *he* looked gorgeous and sexy in his baseball uniform. A twinge of regret lanced through me—wishing it was me keeping score that day.

The nurse kept talking to me, as Sally kept staring—frantic, unglued, her eyes bulging.

That's *her*? He's afraid of *that*? I was afraid of *that*?

It was overload for poor Sally. Like those lunatic therapists who can't function unless they have their screwed up patients to remind them how strong they are.

The shrew was crumbling.

Bram brought a blanket for a walk along a peaceful stream. He surprised me still: "It was that psychic. She really effed things up. I can't believe how much pain I've put you through," as he opened his arms for me to climb into.

He was talking out loud to himself: *"You're the only thing I want to do; everything else is an obligation,"* and then stared at me.

The man I knew from Act I was returning.

"Nancy, take my charge card and get us another place—I wanna move out of that hotel."

"Okay, but where?"

"I don't know—find something you like."

"Please don't ever lie to me again."

"I won't."

He picked up his guitar and began singing—looking at me: *"Starry, starry night… now I understand what you tried to say to me… I'll listen now."*

This time he let the tears fall. ●-●

35

....

FLIMFLAM

It didn't last long. Less than a week.

I asked Lewis why Bram was unable to love. I knew something was stopping him.

"He's terrified of losing his kids," Lewis said.

"But how could anyone lose their kids? His kids love him more than anything."

"Oh, it can happen. Ex-wives can turn the kids against you."

I couldn't imagine a mother turning her kids against their father—a father who was as kind and loving as Bram.

Bram's first wife couldn't have kids and he married his second wife on the rebound, after his first wife remarried. He said they started having kids right away even though they were always fighting.

Lewis then tried to warn me about addiction. That very few people ever stay clean. Lewis did this calmly, knowing any kind of demand would make me rebellious.

Then Bram disappeared.

I called Matt. Matt told me to call the interventionist. But when I called Stallion, he said *he didn't know* who Bram was. I should have realized his disappearance meant he was hiding something.

When Bram resurfaced, I asked him to see Hatshrink. I had met Hatshrink during one of my father's ordeals and he was an expert in meds. When we got to the office, Hatshrink waved us in: "These things usually go faster if you both come in."

I heard things I didn't need to know. Things so personal I shouldn't have been in the room for. Things I never thought I'd hear: "Nancy is horrified I was using heroin — she's probably never going to look at me the same way ever again. My brother told her they found tons of it in the apartment. He also told her I went on a trip with my ex and kids. When I asked him why he told Nancy all that…he just looked at me."

Then I heard the real deal: "After Sally and I got divorced, we'd meet in the city once a week for dinner and sex."

"How could you?" I blurted out (after hearing him say 1000 times how she tricked him).

"I didn't want to lose my family," he whimpered.

"That's *not* what she's asking," Hatshrink intervened.

"Is she very attractive?" Hatshrink asked (completely oblivious to me).

"Well, not as attractive as Nancy, but she's attractive." (I once asked him: "What if she comes out of the bathroom naked when you're there?" He had responded: "I'd throw up. She didn't age well.")

So now I have to hear she's attractive? I sat there dumbfounded. I learned so much about Bram's life; I no longer wondered why he stayed at the carriage house.

The revelations were brutal and he couldn't see how it hurt me—but he was also trusting me, revealing things he never told a soul: "I've never been able to relate to anyone the way I do with Nancy," looking at me with a tear in his eye.

Hatshrink wanted to hear my story next. I wish I'd left. I told Hatshrink how Bram had asked for my hand. How we went house shopping. How we had tried to conceive a dozen times. I told Hatshrink I had broken up with Bram many times but Bram always seemed to want to work it out and have a family with me.

Bram broke in: "You would have started to have kids with someone else if I didn't do all that—you would have had a family *with someone else!*"

When I spoke about Deanna, tears fell. I never cried over Deanna in public. Every day it poured forth driving on the FDR as I worried about my nieces and nephew.

Bram tried rubbing my back, but I was too hurt to let him touch me. More tears fell when I told how Bram broke our engagement. But what I was thinking the whole time was how he had sex with Sally for years after their divorce.

Then Hatshrink asked Bram to leave the room to speak with me privately. He asked me what I thought of my future with Bram.

I said: "There is no future as long as he continues to live in the carriage house. He gets distorted, drinks, does drugs…there's no future this way."

I told Hatshrink I didn't understand why Sally wanted him around all the time, since she's the one who divorced him.

Hatshrink said: "He has all the advantages of a marriage without any of the obligations. It will be very difficult for him to leave."

When I told Leslie this, she said: "What? It's the total opposite. He has more obligations than I've ever heard and not any kind of marriage. That shrink is nuts." She continued: "Nan—come on—Bram's messed up. Even I didn't do *that* drug. It's hard to find someone who doesn't do drugs though. Maybe you go out with men you don't respect because Daddy's such a jerk."

Was it that simple?

After Hatshrink, Bram bolted. He had to get his cell phone from his brother. He mentioned the company locked the doors, and took away his car. He said: "The kids want me to stay in the carriage house for a week; I hope it's okay if we postpone our sleepover."

I told him to stay with his kids from now on and that I hadn't agreed to any sleepover.

Bram still tried to continue for the next two weeks while excluding me from everything. He complained Stallion, his former interventionist and now his current therapist, was a name-dropper consumed with status and appearance. Stallion wrote a book. He was hoping it would lead to that TV show he wanted so badly. The last thing I needed was Bram hiding my existence from an elitist social worker.

"They're going to tell you not to be in a relationship, because that's what therapists do, especially with substance abusers, and I'd rather we broke off now," I told him.

"But I can't talk to anyone the way I can talk to you—you're special," he said.

It went from "you're the only thing I want to do" to the generic *special*.

Just a few days ago he was telling the staff we were engaged.

Bram kept filling me in—he had to pee in a cup, in front of Stallion, three times a week. He had found himself a new abuser.

The last time I spoke with Bram was after a nightmare I had:

We were in group therapy—my mother was the therapist. Bram didn't sit next to me, but lay down on a chair, rocking back and forth like a baby. I ran out.

A woman came out of the room after me. She had long dark hair. She wouldn't show me her eyes. I ran after her, trying to see her eyes. I finally saw them. They were vampire eyes—luminous white sclera and red splotches where the irides and pupils were supposed to be.

It was the psycho psychic who had betrayed me.

I called Bram after the dream.

"Everything's *greaaaat*. I'm moving out of the hotel to a more convenient place downtown, closer to the ferry for my kids, and closer to work. But I smoked a little weed that showed up in my urine, so even though my brother gets high and Janet gets high, I have to wait another week before they let me come back to work. Do you want to get together?"

"Well, when you have time in your schedule, you can give me a call," I said.

"Okay—or you can call me," he replied. ◗●

36

....

PRIVATE PLANES

Now that I knew Bram was on major drugs the past two years, I questioned everything. Was he high when he proposed? High at Miraval? High at my breast surgery? Everything had an extra level of deception. He wasn't scratching at Miraval and his sleep was peaceful and his eyes were normal.

I remembered that day in the new apartment a year after we'd met—with his back turned to me—not moving, just sitting at the table. He must have been *coming down*.

It must have started before the hole in his leg. Yes—that made sense. The night before my shoulder surgery when he smoked that joint saying he wanted a Rabbi at our wedding—it wasn't a joint.

That was around the time his mom began her final decline. Months later, when I asked if he was on coke after he kissed me. When he fell before Thanksgiving and broke his pinky.

The hand surgeon looked at his bloody arms but said nothing. *How did they operate on his finger without testing for drugs?*

I knew Leslie's drug use never impaired her ability to love deeply—but Bram never learned how to love.

Thanksgiving passed. Deanna's birthday was November 30th, and the anniversary of her death a few days later. I had not cried for weeks, but I could not stop crying on this day.

I was driving to a writing class in the city, going 75 mph because I was late. I noticed someone called 8:00 a.m. It was Sunday. It was a faraway number. Probably that stupid fax number beeping into my cell again.

I listened to the message heading onto the 59th Street Bridge:

"Hi Nancy—I'm in California—I partied a little over Thanksgiving and it showed up in my urine. I'll be here for 30 days. I didn't want you to think I was ignoring you. I know you understand. Please call back and tell me you got this message. I'll try you next weekend. I love you."

I called Matt, not realizing how much he enjoyed tormenting me or why.

"Yes he's back in rehab. Sally flew down with him and she's going back in a week with the kids to visit him."

"Are they married?" I feared Bram and Sally never finalized their divorce.

"I don't know what's going on with them, but I have to get ready for Norm's wedding somewhere in the Five Towns."

Bram's father was remarrying less than two years since his wife passed. Matt knew I lived in the Five Towns; he knew Bram and I had been engaged. *I can feel your smile through the phone.*

I called Bram's number with the wind knocked out of me: "Hi Bram— your brother said Sally went with you, so I'm not sure why you called. You'll get well if you want to. Good Luck." ●●

37

....

PLAYBACK

Leslie gave a high pitched screech at 1:00 a.m.: *"I'm falling, I'm falling."*

I closed my door. Then I heard a crash. I still didn't get up. Then I heard my father's shuffled footsteps going to see what happened. I never went down. I went to sleep.

I drove into the city the next day to get an apartment away from my family. I saw a one-bedroom apartment, looked no more than five minutes, and said: "I'll take it yesterday."

My commute would be 20 minutes. There was a rooftop pool. I hadn't begun to feel guilt about Leslie — that would come like a brick soon enough.

I ventured downstairs to do laundry, *two days after* Leslie fell and hit her head. It smelled funny.

The second time, I brought room spray to rid the strange odor while I finished my loads. She stared at me, while I mumbled what an asshole she was. I couldn't tell what the musty unusual smell was.

It wasn't until the next night that I realized she hadn't moved. Sitting up with perfect posture — naked — on the wrong end of her bed, staring at me with an expression I never saw before.

"What are you doing? What is wrong with you? *Are you sitting in urine?*"

I still didn't get it.

"Put something on. Cover yourself now!"

"No," she kept replying.

Finally she admitted, she didn't get up to go to the bathroom.

"I'm calling 911 right now, if you don't get in the shower."

One week prior this had worked—I got her into the shower just by screaming. She said: "I won't be able to get out." I told her to shut up and went upstairs.

Now the game changed. I didn't realize she wasn't faking it before. This time she was much worse. A switch had flipped. She had gone over the edge into a mudslide.

By the time the police came, she was lying down, saying her back was broken. I didn't have the energy to tell them she'd just been sitting up.

One of the cops wouldn't stop smiling, while Leslie was fighting not to go with them. They wrapped her like a mummy and carried her out on a stretcher.

I asked: "Why are you smiling? *Please stop smiling.*"

"I'm not smiling," the cop said still smiling.

I said: "Why can't you stop smiling even now?"

The next day Leslie was in a foul condition. She told me they wanted to ECT her. She was lying half on and half off a couch in the visitors lounge when she said this. I finally got her to sit up by sitting on her head—she had to move. Then I got a nice inpatient to grab one hand, while I grabbed the other, and we walked her into her room, with her gown wide open in the back and her figure looking rather sensual considering the circumstances.

I came home that night and began to play back all the times I had a chance. All the times she asked me to hang out. All those nights she was alone and had no one. Would I ever get another chance?

I'd make it up to her if only she'd recover. I could live with her playing piano, working out, going to dinner—what the divorced alimony wives did. Plenty of women don't work and don't wind up in the nut house.

When I said hello to her roommate, Les said: "Nan—don't talk to her, don't look at her—she's a lunatic." My big sister—still protecting me.

Then Leslie closed her eyes and put her fingers in her ears, so she didn't have to hear me...begging her to eat. ●●

38

....

SURPRISES

I went to visit Leslie for the fourth time. I knew she was getting better, just from the way she was picking her teeth. Her facial expression had changed—she had one.

She also started talking. But it was the same question again and again:

"What if a person could live forever?"

I kept saying no, but she was persistent.

"What if they could?"

"Okay," I relented.

"They would be really fat," she said.

I knew where she was going.

"No, they'd be really skinny," I reassured her.

"How?"

"Because their metabolism would have to be so superior for them to live forever."

Then she quieted down and thought about it:

"Would they be lopsided? What if they were lopsided?"

"Well, the world would be lopsided too, so they'd be straight."

"How could the world be lopsided?"

"If someone could live forever then the world would be so different, it would have to be lopsided," and I drifted sideways off the bed and became a lopsided person walking in a lopsided world.

This one thought of living forever seemed to torture her. Maybe she'll have to live forever without Deanna. Does she feel guilty? Does she have some real underlying fear?

She said her hands were too weak to eat, so I asked if I should bring her a milkshake. She said yes. When I came back with two, she said it would give her the worst reflux, and that she just wanted to look at it. The nurses poured it into tiny little cups for the other patients.

The social worker called Friday and said they were discharging Leslie on Monday. She asked if I wanted to pick her up and to bring some clothes, but no underwear.

"We made a bargain with Leslie. She has agreed to go to a counseling center."

"Okay. Who's going to take her back and forth to this center?" I inquired.

"Well, we don't know about that."

I went to visit Les expecting to find a 75% improvement. Instead she told me to leave, take the clothes back, and asked: "What's this?" when I handed her house keys.

I called Perl: "Do you understand what I'm dealing with?"

"You don't have to explain Nan, I get it. They're discharging her with-out an aide or a nurse?—*oh boy*."

"I wish I could fly Leslie out to you," I told him.

"Maybe they'd be more humane here in Oregon, but I doubt it— they're all focused on medicine."

"You mean pills, right?"

"Yep."

Leslie was finally discharged. Two days later she asked me to take her to another hospital. Then she wanted to leave as soon as we got there. We were surrounded by misfits, and I don't mean the other patients. Les said we should go. *Why didn't I listen to her?* Because she also told me she was being hypnotized. How could I tell the difference between what she knew and what she fantasized?

I agreed and said if the shrink was bad, we'd leave.

An enormous woman sat too close to Leslie and began scolding her about hygiene. Then an MD—with his hair gelled and his body reek-ing of cologne—asked Leslie what holiday just passed. Valentine's Day. I didn't know myself. There was another worker sitting in a chair, no expression, no reaction—the type his neighbors describe as: "kept to himself, never bothered anyone," after police found 10 dead people in his home.

I wanted to visit Les in the all-female unit she was assigned to. The psy-chiatric nurse wanted to discuss her history but couldn't give me di-rections and disconnected me when she put me on hold. Then I asked what the visiting hours were but she didn't know that either.

When I arrived, there was a large plaque with the hours printed in bold letters on the front door she walked through every day. It took over five minutes to unlock three doors. I wondered how they'd escape from a fire.

After half an hour, she let me say hello to my sister. Leslie zombied into the TV room. There was one chair. It was dark. Bram's rehab had lush gardens, an enormous indoor pool, a gym, computer room—lake. I asked if the shrink had spoken with Leslie.

"No."

"Leslie has not had a consultation with the psychiatrist?"

"She's seen her."

"You mean, she saw Leslie down the hall? But she has not spoken with her?"

"This is how it's done now—I'm the psychiatric nurse and I consult with the psychiatrist about all the patients."

I said I wanted to take Leslie out.

"She's in no condition to be home. The only way Leslie can be discharged is if she wears clothes instead of her gown, attends three groups a day, and stays out of her room for four hours daily."

She hadn't done that in 15 years. How would they understand a woman who never shaved, hated bras, and played five hours of piano every day most of her life? The fact that Leslie wasn't befriending everyone meant she was returning to her saner self.

My mother said: "Get her out of that place," and "My feet are killing me."

"Why is your nightgown dirty?"

"Because he wouldn't let me take a shower today and change it."

"Dad, would you please get normal? I need you now. Please. Leslie is so ill."

"Do you think I'll live much longer?" he asked. He was just turning 78.

"Do you want to?" was my obnoxious reply.

"I know I'm nuts. I'll try."

It was the sanest thing he'd said in months.

If I knew Leslie was going to be in the hospital I wouldn't have taken the lease for the new apartment and when I asked to get out of it, they said no. The commute to the office would be easier but now I had to be close to Long Island for Leslie.

Again I asked if Leslie could be switched to a different unit, *above ground*.

"I'm sorry she's not in a penthouse," the nurse replied.

The nurse began petitioning the court to inject Leslie with meds. Leslie was allergic to the injected meds, but that was irrelevant. The drugs were making her eyes bulge.

The last time I visited her, she said: "You're not my sister," but took the three chocolate bars and two bran muffins I brought.

I spoke with an attorney for the state. He told me there was nothing I could do.

Perl told me to find an 'Ombudsman.' *A what?* Patient advocate. So I called the hospital and they switched me to quality control. They had no patient advocate. I called the county.

When I next saw Leslie there was a mound of crumpled cookie by her feet.

"What happened?"

"That aide over there crushed a cookie in my hand."

"That *huge* guy put his hand on yours and *crushed your fingers over it?*"

"Yeah — he's crazy."

"Why?"

"He said I stole it, but I didn't — that girl gave it to me."

The mentally ill don't deserve respect. Things can be done to the mentally ill that deserve jail time. But who would believe you?

She looked at me: "Why are your eyes moving?"

Maybe she isn't that ill. Then she told me she broke her urethra masturbating and scheduled an appointment with the urologist. *Maybe she does need more meds.*

I started to get faint circles all over my body. It wasn't ringworm but what could it be? I even had a ring on the tip of my nose. I had two little matching rings on both sides of my upper lip and various sized rings all over my arms and chest.

I went back to my rheumatologist. I wanted to show him the rings. But before he came into the room, my record was wide open facing me: "...*large mass* left hepatic lobe."

He tried telling me it wasn't cancer, but just to be sure: "Let's do a contrast MRI."

I got nervous for five minutes and then didn't care. That's when I realized my weakness over breakups and animals came from another dimension. If I could be this strong, maybe I could rewire about guys and pets.

Out of the blue, I got a ghost text…from Bram: "I think about you a lot. Maybe you'd like to get together some time?"

That's how he reconnects? With a text?

Was he playing it cool with me?

He followed with a phone call: "I have a building I want to sell you—do you remember?" as if it were four years ago and we were just beginning.

When we met, I tried to hide how much I wanted to be in his arms. We met in a public place—just in case. I asked what happened. I shouldn't have.

"I realize my ex is the reason for a lot my problems. I'm sorry it's taken me this long—I've been trying to work out my shit. When I got back from my last rehab, I told Sally I didn't want a relationship with her."

"What are you talking about?" (I instantly saw them having sex—recently. *Were the gold shoes hers after all?*)

"I guess she hoped when I got clear, I'd want to be with her."

Right, especially since you had sex again when you weren't with me. Did he go down on her? What kind of sex was it? Did they have passionate, angry sex, or was it one of those depressing times when there's no one else around and no smiles when it's over?

The next night we met for dinner but he asked to meet half way: "I thought it would be romantic to accidentally meet and walk through the city," as he smiled with his face all sweaty. ●●

39

....

ONE IN-ONE OUT

The next day my liver films came in—a giant hemangioma taking up the entire left lobe.

Four hours after finding out about my mass, Leslie's nurse called to say they were having a hearing in the morning, to transfer Leslie to a state hospital. I got them to delay by an hour so I could do my cats' insulin.

I spoke with the Director of Psychiatry, who said: "Leslie is a great candidate for ECT."

"My family isn't into that—if she forgot one chord, one line, she'd want to jump."

He reassuringly said: "We have a Philharmonic timpanist who's on our video advertising ECT—and she's had it *many, many* times."

"Did you hear what you just said? If it worked, why did she need it so often?"

No answer.

"I must tell you that Leslie noticed my nystagmus when two MDs failed to detect it."

"So—what's your point?" he snapped back refusing to admit Leslie might be more aware than he wanted. I wasn't sure what the point of the hearing was, if these were the schmucks I'd be dealing with.

I went to see Dr. Bowtie hoping for a miracle—that he'd rescue Leslie. Lewis had recommended this psychiatrist to try and get Leslie into a Manhattan hospital. Bowtie's office was in the 90s by Central Park, on a block lined with townhouses. Was this where Jewish WASP wannabe shrinks got good deals 30 years ago? Or their parents left them an apartment they converted into an office?

When I got to the townhouse, I didn't realize I had been gazing at the doorbell, until someone pushed past me into the building.

There was another name which shared Bowtie's doorbell and I was transfixed by it. Out of all the offices, buildings, townhouses, streets in Manhattan—not possible.

Stallion? Stallion's office was here? Stallion shared a doorbell with Bowtie?

Actually they shared the same suite.

I called Bram. Maybe there was another therapist by that name. "You see we're soulmates and the universe is conspiring to bring us together, whether we want it to or not," he mocked.

I walked into Bowtie's office and lost whatever calm I had. I told him about Stallion, Bram, the drugs—before I could get to Leslie. Bowtie started laughing.

I imagined the 6'5" Stallion social worker rolling his eyes at the 5'3" Bowtie shrink who shared his suite. How did a brilliant MD share a suite with a dummy Goliath social worker who earned 10 times as much, and never get offended? And how was this happening?

A doubt rose within me too. I noticed that Bowtie was a trope—his left eye turned inward and he was insecure and trying to hide it with tinted lenses. But I pushed these doubts away because I had to trust someone. Bowtie showed me a side staircase to exit, so I could avoid Stallion.

I wished Bram and I had never met four years ago. That we could meet now, when all the promises hadn't been broken.

The next day he called for dinner and mentioned my portable closets: "Please let me buy you some furniture—at least a couch."

"You want to make amends to me?" I asked.

He shouted: "I already said I was sorry. Do you want me to grovel? It has nothing to do with you. It doesn't matter how *you* feel. It's to make *ME* feel better. It doesn't matter if you forgive me—it's **Step Nine!** If you can't accept that, it's too bad."

"Don't worry, I don't want any more than you can give. I don't want you at all," I said.

Step Nine? You don't apologize to people you screwed over to make yourself feel better. Words won't do. You want to make amends? Volunteer at a burn unit.

I went to the hearing. There were more people than I expected: the psychiatric nurse, director, temporary shrink, and state lawyer. Leslie wouldn't get out of bed—her legs wouldn't work. I told her to get out of bed or she would never come home again.

"Okay, did you bring me the sunflower seeds?" she asked.

We sat in an office that was nonexistent when the nurse took Leslie's history in the public lounge. The nurse was nervous, her voice shaking: "Leslie refuses to take her meds."

Leslie and I protested. Leslie said: "I'm taking everything except the higher dose of Lithium. It's too much. It makes me feel funny."

That sounded very reasonable. I had seen her reactions when she was on too high a dose. The director waved his hand like a hammer, shushing us.

The nurse said: "She's not making it to group."

"Yes I am," Leslie retorted. "I'm going to three, just not five. I can't sit. I hurt my urethra with the vibrator. *You know what a vibrator is?*" she asked, turning toward the nurse.

Leslie suddenly sprung from the room. The director continued as if we were in court: "No, No, No, let me finish!" he insisted. "ECT is the favored option here."

I didn't ask how much each dose made for the hospital.

Let's see: $500 a shock—three shocks a week—nine shocks conservatively and all the remaining visits.

After reading my three-page letter of their many HIPAA violations, he said: "I'll transfer her to Melloman." When I rushed to tell Leslie the good news, she said: "Oh, I can't go. I have friends here. I like it here."

"Do you care about me at all, do you love me? I need surgery. I need you to go to this new unit today. Please don't do this to me," I pleaded.

"I'll go if you promise I'll be out in a week."

"Yes, I promise," I lied.

The state lawyer met me outside and after fumbling for a cigarette, said: "I'd trust Melloman with my life. These other shrinks are horrible. I see them in court. If anyone can get her better it's him. I've seen him do miracles on the worst cases."

"Do you think she needs shock?"

"*Noooo*, that's for people who are catatonic and just lying there."

I went back and asked the staff to please give Leslie some of the sunflower seeds they confiscated.

I had a dream that night:

Leslie was down a huge tunnel cave — with a guy with a knife. We were in a Grand Canyon type place but with mountains and steep drops everywhere. I told her she had to come with me before the killer woke up.

I lay on my back and put her on top of me, so we were both facing upward. She couldn't move her body so I clung her to me so she wouldn't fall down the drop. I held my arms under her arms, encircling her, while I dug my feet in hard. I had Schwarzenegger legs and pushed us up the long tunnel, backwards, one leg at a time. It had a 30-degree slope and we were moving on a slippery forest floor.

"Wow Nan, I never knew you were this strong." It wasn't easy in my dream. I was fiercely powerful. We finally reached the top. I had to make sure it was safe.

I tiptoed, checking the cabins surrounding us. It was a resort and people were eating dinner. Fresh from the oven chocolate chip cookies were everywhere. We made it.

The next day when I went to work, the big one had called. Melloman left a wonderful message that he was going to do everything possible to save my sister.

I felt great hope. ●●

40

....

THE HACKER

B ram called again: "Can we meet for dinner?"

"I really don't think it's a good idea. I'm under too much pressure. I have to get ready for my surgery and Leslie is very ill."

"What's the matter with her? What *surgery?*"

"I don't want to talk about it. I'm trying to lease my building but Bubbles keeps backing out of the deal."

"What if *I give you* the money every month for your practice?"

"Are you serious?"

"Don't worry about anything. I'll help you."

A wave of relief washed over me — a huge weight lifted off of my shoulders. All the feelings returned from when he used to make promises and I believed him.

I went to see Dr. Myron Schwartz at Mount Sinai. Arthur Wolintz had said my hemangioma was gigantic: "Don't do it Nancy. You could bleed out."

But I was getting that humongous ball of blood out of me.

Schwartz came into his exam room and took a look at my films: "Oh this is nothing. You can leave it in, unless you plan on having a baby."

"Well, I wanted a baby but never found the right man."

At that point he shifted, his entire body moved, and his mouth dropped open: "What do you mean?"

"Just what I said. I never found anyone I'd want to be my baby's father and the one person I wanted—well—he chose drugs over me."

"But you're beautiful, you're smart, I can see you're a good person—I don't get it."

I couldn't help it—I started tearing up. Suddenly he took my hand. I started crying more. He did not let go of my hand. Something in me elevated when he took my hand. This incredible man had my back.

"Well—we can do it laparoscopically so you can still have a baby if you want. It's big enough that it could rupture and both you and the baby would be in trouble—we should take it out," he concurred.

Bram kept calling. He kept offering to help. Finally he yelled: "I said I offered to help you—with your office, your surgery that you won't tell me about."

I awoke sweating at 4:00 a.m., after a dream that Sally was pregnant. I fell back asleep only to awake from another one—that Bram and Sally were still married and Sally and I were on the phone for an hour talking about their marriage. She was explaining that they never really divorced.

I was afraid of hating Bram. I didn't want to hate him, I wanted something to fix it.

He asked to go for a walk again. He asked to meet half way. It was strange. Was he renewing our courtship?

We went back to the same Italian restaurant on Second with just the right ambiance and the Spanish themed colors I loved. We ordered a Caesar salad for two, along with our main courses. When I ordered gnocchi, Bram's sarcasm returned:

"You always order the same thing. Can't you try something else? Don't hang your bag on the wine bottle. Why can't you ever put your bag on the floor?"

He was smiling the entire time.

"How long do you need to one-up me, before you can relax?" I asked. I was too tired for games.

"Did you go to the obstetrician?"

"The *what?*"

"Oh sorry I meant—um, what test did you have?"

"Do you realize what you just said?"

"Yeah, baby doctor. I had a dream last night that my mother told me not to have any more kids because she didn't want to take care of them. But I said: 'I'll take care of it Mom.'"

"You're talking about kids again with me? Do you realize your dream means your mom wouldn't want you to have more?"

"Nancy, didn't you hear me? I said I'd take care of the baby. Only I want to live in the carriage house five more years until all my kids go to college."

"Then that's what you should do, and find another Nancy when they're gone."

"There is no other Nancy."

The waiter came over and began elaborately making the Caesar salad we ordered. The man at the neighboring table was looking at me. Suddenly the mood changed. Bram took my long necklace out of my shirt to fall along my breasts and stared at me.

Then he took my hand: "Tell me what you need."

"I've never been in this position before. My parents are running out of money. They'll have nothing in two years. I'd like you to help me get an apartment, like you once offered. I will pay you back either when I sell my building or sell their house. And I'm ashamed to ask this."

"That would be a lot," said the man who had made millions the past year.

"How were you able to buy your mansion in two weeks and your half a million golf club membership, and everything else since I've known you? How much have you spent renting hotel rooms for four years and the extra 300K your employees get every year for the rest of their lives? Did any of them take your feces to be examined? I wouldn't need to ask you, if I'd never met you. I'd have 200K more right now. You broke every promise. Why did you offer to buy my old apartment?"

"I didn't break any promises," looking down at his Diet Coke.

"Really? So that's our little two-year-old running around over there? And we'll drive back to our beautiful home? The engagement ring is on my finger, not in the vault?"

He looked straight at me: "Okay—you're right."

He called again for dinner the next week. Again he said he would help: "Please meet with me."

We took a walk by the East River and he started to sing and hug me. The water was rushing by, few people were on the promenade—it was the perfect night.

"I'm so healthy I'm going to live forever. I went to a nutritionist Madonna couldn't even get an appointment with," he said.

"Since when are you a name-dropper? How did you find this great nutritionist?"

"Sally went there and—well, do you want me to lie?"

"Do you have dinner with Sally and the kids now?" I started walking away.

"Yes—but only very recently."

"Did Stallion encourage this?" I started walking faster, getting closer to my building.

"Yes."

"So I guess when your daughter gets kicked in the back by her alcoholic husband, and her little girl is watching, it's okay she sits down to dinner with him. Do your kids know you're here?"

"It would upset them if they saw us together."

"What do you mean?" I stopped and turned.

"You didn't get along with them, *Nancy*."

"But they see Sally with her boyfriend, right?"

"Yes."

I tried thinking through the pain. I remember the last time he mentioned his kids, they thought I was cute in the old camp photo he showed them. Nothing changed since then, except one thing: Sally had seen me at the rehab.

The nurse's voice: "Bram's in the cottages."

Sally swinging around—her eyes bulging, fearful—her enormous frown. It was too late to stop my smile with the nurse before she saw me.

I imagined her rage at being told Bram's fiancée was there, since that's what he was telling the entire staff. I imagined her going home, screaming to the kids: "You better tell your father you hate Nancy—that you can't stand her."

Maybe they thought I was stealing their dad away all the time he wasn't with me either. Or maybe they just hated me.

"Did you tell Stallion we were engaged?"

"No."

"Why?"

"I don't talk about old relationships," said with tight eyes and no smile.

"Even though you were calling me your fiancée the week before you saw him?" as I felt my heart in my stomach.

"Nancy, I want to build this relationship back up and see where it goes."

"You want to see where it goes? While you're waking up next door to Sally?"

"If I don't sleep in the carriage house every night, Sally would go to court to change the visitation rights." *I know that's not true.*

He was sleeping in the city three times a week—it seemed his *'therapy'* regressed him. Did Stallion want him to stay ill? He was getting $400/hr.

"Stay there five more years. I wish you luck. I need people who want me around."

He walked me up to my apartment. The pain was too great. I figured I'd never see him again. He knew. He could see it. Suddenly I had the power.

We began kissing. He never kissed me so passionately or for so long. He was a completely different lover and all over me. After he satisfied me I couldn't return the favor. I just couldn't do it. I wanted to but I couldn't break from the thought of Sally satisfying him, or some other woman he'd been with.

I didn't want to cry in front of him so I asked him to leave. He called later, begging to come back.

A few days later he sent an email: "I don't want to lose you. What can I do to help?"

I needed his help badly but he wasn't acting on his offer. Next he shouted into the phone: "You refuse to see me."

I got off the phone before he started cursing and because someone was on call waiting. Another hang-up. Only two people had my new number: Morda and Bram.

Since I gave it to Bram, I was receiving hang-ups. Angry calls with no one on the other end who would repeatedly smash the phone down. The last phone call was the worst—they just stayed on the line… *not* hanging up. I couldn't resist: "I hope you're having fun."

I hung up and shut the ringer off. I refused to give weight to this odorless venom.

She had done this in my office. A lot. I never bothered Bram about it. I figured it would only give energy to her madness. She once called 10 times in a row as: "an old friend, I want to surprise her."

Morda put the phone to my ear because this *'old friend'* refused to say who she was. I recognized her voice from some of the volatile messages Bram would play for me.

The next time he called: "I'm your friend. Don't worry about anything. I need glasses. Can I come to your office tomorrow?"

I sent him a confrontational email, but later on told him not to read it—if he didn't want to hate me. When he arrived he said: "I didn't read the email yet."

"Yes you did. It was read at 10:53 last night."

"No. I never read it. I swear."

"Well, someone is reading our emails then."

After the exam, we discussed our childhoods and our parents' relationships. "I can't handle deception. I didn't grow up like that."

"Well—maybe I have trouble believing you really have my back," he softly replied.

"Then you'll never be the right guy for me, because I've had it this whole time, and you've never had mine. Maybe you could say *'Thank you.'*"

The next day he asked me to send him more emails to see if someone else would open them. He had told me his ex hacked his computers during their divorce. I sent him my own email too. An email of all the dates I missed at work cataloging all of his crises, doctor visits, and hospital stays. I figured if he had an aversion to emotion, the lawyer in him could still understand numbers. He texted if I wanted it transferred into my account or in a check.

I happily responded: "A check."

Not waiting until he changed his mind, I met him at his hotel. He opened the door wearing a T-shirt from Miraval and smiling. We ordered dinner and he sang *Desperado: "you better come to your senses."* Then he went into his bedroom and came out with a check.

"Are you disappointed?" he asked.

"Yes. You spent more than this renting that penthouse for a month. I wish I didn't need it. I wish I could give you money."

The thought of taking money from anyone was so abhorrent to me that I had to continuously remind myself it was money I lost *because* of him. I felt doubly sick because I felt ungrateful. The check wouldn't solve any problems. My taxes just went up by 28K. But what saddened me most was the obvious. We were still at a hotel.

At dinner he told me: "My sisters want a piece of the company. Alexa said she didn't think her son should have to ask my son for a job later on."

"But why don't they have a piece? They should have a share and they don't need a reason or a child to justify it. It has nothing to do with her son. And her son *should* have to ask your son for a job since you're the one who made the company four times as profitable and she never worked a day there."

He didn't notice my sigh, as I realized we'd never have one peaceful evening because someone would always be on his back.

"Nancy—a lot has changed. I don't want to get upset thinking about it. I'm just glad you're here."

"Do your sisters think you're going to drop dead? Can't you postpone the meeting? I'm worried all this stress is the last thing you need."

"Well—I'm no longer CEO. My brother is."

"Oh—that's great—you can finally focus on your health."

He stopped eating and looked at me: "You're not mad I'm not CEO? That's really refreshing to hear. Everyone's so angry with me."

"Why would I be mad? I'm relieved—"

I wondered how Matt could take it by default instead of holding it for his older brother, all the while hiring Stallion to humiliate Bram. I watched Bram's inner turmoil as he looked up—seeing my face express his heart.

"How much did the business prosper since you were running the company?"

"It went from 4% to 16%," he said with a proud smile.

"What would have happened if you didn't come back to take over 25 years ago?"

"The company would have probably assigned an overseer, when my dad got ill."

"Don't buy anyone's love—that's what you do. Go into that meeting strong."

"Is that what I'm doing with you? Buying your love?"

I looked away: "You still don't get it. I lost money with you. I lost a fortune and let's not talk about what else I lost. It's the opposite, Bram— I'm the one who gave to you what you can't buy."

Then he opened his laptop to make sure he had enough funds in the account for the amount he wrote me. I peered over his shoulder. He covered the screen, but then he put his hand down. There were several accounts. One was in both his name and Sally's.

"What's that account with her?"

"That's for repairs to the house."

"Can she see your other accounts like we are now?"

"No."

"How long will that account exist?"

"Until the kids are 21. I think I can give you another check in a month and then something every two weeks."

"How come you were able to buy your mansion so quickly and all the other things?"

"It's not like that anymore."

"Oh."

I felt awful. I didn't realize it was something he had to calculate. He always had access to millions, but now Matt had that power. Ironically Bram was incredibly frugal before his drug use. Before he lost his mom. He never took advantage of his wealth. He was incredibly responsible—the way you are when you've *worked* for your success.

"Come on, let's lie down for a while," he said.

"Did you sleep with anyone the past six months?" I didn't want to know.

He shook his head without looking at me. He was lying. Before I knew it, all my clothes were off, and we were in Bram's favorite position.

Again I got satisfied, twice, but it began to go further. He was like a dog in heat. I hadn't had real sex in over a year. I had to give insulin to my cats. He knew I had to leave. We never had rushed sex. Suddenly we were making love.

"Say it."

"I love you," he acquiesced.

I pulled away and got dressed.

"I'm single, totally single." I said it out loud—confirming for myself. "Find someone else to have sex with—I can't do this."

"Do you think I don't care about you, if I gave you that check?"

"That's making up for a fraction of what I lost."

"No, I don't owe you anything. I gave you that, because *I care* Nancy."

He gave me cab money—in hundreds. It was almost $1000. Then he went back to his bag and gave me a few more. I sank to the floor—all the energy leaving me.

He walked me downstairs with his arm around me. He hugged me tightly in the street. When the cab arrived I got in and turned to say goodbye, but he was already gone.

He called the next day and said with a cracked voice: "I love you."

I didn't know what to say—he was feeling it out.

"I want to come Monday to try on glasses again. Last night was great. Are you okay about it? Are you upset?"

It was July 4th weekend. We always spent it together. I felt enormous relief he wasn't traveling somewhere with unknown (or known) some-ones.

"I don't know—I'm just scared." It was the truth.

When I got to the office the next day, I took a look at his insurance card. Sally was on it—it was a family plan. All the kids' names were on it too.

Then I opened my inbox, and there were 15 messages someone else had read and saved. I showed Morda. When I hit the screen the emails disappeared.

I called Bram and asked if he wanted me to hire a private investigator. He did.

I texted him to see if he still planned to come to the office Monday— *the day he asked to come.* He texted back immediately: "It's a three-day weekend. I won't be around. I'll call you later. I love you."

"Are you traveling?"

"YES." In caps.

Several patients had asked me that very day if I was 'traveling' for 4th of July. His "I won't be around" threw me. I had prepared myself for his traveling with her. I was purposely keeping a distance. I could have handled it if we didn't have sex. But his recent intimacy left me feeling powerless, used—my head started to burn.

Before I unleashed a barrage of texts…I paused.

Morda said: "Traveling means plane or boat—send it to the mother-fucker."

During my stream of insults he tried to call and then texted: "I meant I was driving…where do you think I'm going? Where do I always go? I'm going to New Jersey."

So I never got the chance to tell Bram the private investigator laughed when Morda asked who hacked our emails: "The ex-wife of course! Did he ever use your computer to read his own email? She hacked into his and got into yours that way. You gotta get an Apple—they never get hacked."

Bram could lie about anything, or rather omit the truth as he saw it. But it's not okay if you react—you're not allowed to crack his facade. He never realized the impact it produced—you just never know what's true.

Why didn't he just say he was driving…why don't people talk anymore? After surviving everything—one single misunderstood text—and it was over.

Then Morda started laughing—the person who told me I was a sister to her. The woman I bailed out of a 30K charge card debt. And in an instant I knew—Bram wasn't the only one with saboteurs.

I had my liver surgery a few weeks later. Dr. Schwartz sat on my bed and schmoozed, casually drinking a cup of coffee. No big deal cutting out half of my liver. When he got up, he kissed my cheek.

Then they wheeled us down the runway with residents standing on both sides, waiting for which one of us they'd get to see stripped of all dignity. After the surgery, Schwartz came to visit and sat on my bed and kissed my cheek. It made me feel that odd feeling.

Acceptance. ●●

41

....

OBJECTION

*W*ould I ever go to bed and wake up with the bad breath of someone lying next to me? Would I ever drool on my pillow and feel his damp hair smeared into it? Where was my partner who didn't snore and had a sexy chest I could kiss goodnight?

After Leslie was discharged, a caseworker visited her. "Nan, she didn't even knock. She just opened the door into my room."

"What do you mean?"

"I don't know. She just came in and spoke to me for five minutes and left, saying: 'See you later babe.'"

Lewis explained: "Entitlement of Entrance."

"So there's no respect for a mentally ill person?" I asked.

"Right."

"Why?"

"It's crazy."

The following day Morda came into my office to hand me the phone. She had a concerned look—she was already clued in to the level of Leslie's different cries for help. I got on the phone.

"Nan I called 911. They're taking me to the hospital."

"But you've only been home three weeks. Wait! I'll come get you. *Please don't go.*"

"Okay—come get me."

The phone rang again. Morda had that look as she handed it to me.

"Nan, the police are here," my father shouted.

"Put me on with them."

"Oh—I can't go down there again."

"Lenny, take the phone to the officer," I heard my mother desperately pleading because she couldn't walk.

"No, I can't go down again."

"Take the phone!" she yelled.

With the speaker on, I heard him go downstairs, give the phone to Leslie instead of the officer, where she promptly hung up. I called back. It all repeated. Finally he gave it to the police officer. They were taking her back to Franklin.

Two weeks later my father called the office on a Saturday—he was frantic: "There's a special delivery letter for you."

"Open it."

"It's about Leslie."

Later that day I got a call from the social worker: "I just wanted to tell you, we're having a hearing this Tuesday to give Leslie 'meds over objection.'"

Meaning they can strap her down and inject her.

I had no idea what meds she was on. I didn't want to go, but told Morda to reschedule.

Eight months had elapsed since I last spoke with Perlstein. I had to discuss what drugs would be safest for Leslie.

He said: "Nan, it's time for you to take care of yourself and for Leslie to accept the consequences of her actions. Somehow Leslie has to take responsibility—it has to come from her."

"I'll feel guilty if I do that."

"Why?"

"Well won't I be abandoning her then?"

"Who abandoned who?"

I called Perl at 1:00 a.m., happy he was on the West Coast. He had me go through the list of drugs they wanted to force into Leslie.

Haldol, Zyprexa, Cogentin, Lithium—the list went on. It sounded like a chemical lobotomy.

Perl said: "Why don't you see if they'll discharge her to you?"

"They told me that was impossible," I said, surprised he had any hope.

"Well—it doesn't hurt to ask," he said.

I was amazed that he was encouraging this.

On Monday, the lawyer was kind enough to call me back: "I want to tell you they won't give her all those meds—that's just a list of alternatives if some don't work." I relaxed a bit.

"Well—Perlstein said maybe she could be discharged."

"I don't think they'll consider that," she said.

"He said it couldn't hurt to ask." I was sounding weaker from her doubt.

"Well then I've got to run and get the forms and get started on this," as she rushed off the phone. *Huh? She was going to try?*

When I arrived at the hospital, an attractive skinny woman with very long blond hair and exquisite fashion sense looked at me: "Nancy?"

It was my killer lawyer. *Well, alright!*

Then I saw the man who almost killed my father, who now wanted to kill my sister. He had an Italian sounding name, but was from Argentina. He was in his early 80s with perfectly coiffed white hair blown back with hair spray. He had a chronic smile and no words came out of it.

When we entered the conference room, the court officer told me where to sit. The chairs were old, stained, and the room smelled moldy. There was one window that probably hadn't been opened in 50 years.

The doctor was first sworn in. I can't recall all his exact words, but his description of Leslie was dire.

He went through the list of meds and contrary to what my lawyer had told me, wanted to give all of them to Leslie.

Then Leslie appeared. She looked at me—I smiled encouragingly. She was agitated and had a rash on part of her face.

Our lawyer asked the doctor: "Is it possible the rash we are seeing to-day, is the rash Leslie said the Effexor gives her? The very rash we are seeing right now?"

He shrugged: "I don't think it is a rash. She doesn't bathe."

"I took a shower last night," Leslie interjected.

"Objection!"

"Is it possible Doctor—that the aches and muscle spasms Leslie says she has are from some of these very meds you want her to take? That she refuses to take?"

It was my turn. The court officer motioned me where to sit and I was sworn in. The doctor and I had a stare-down. I couldn't believe it. When I took my seat he was staring at me with the smile that had been on his face the entire morning.

Even when he gave his testimony, he smiled. But he continued to look at me, so I gave it right back to him. I wasn't smiling. I did the best glare I could, but he remained immobile—not even a flinch.

The lawyer asked me several questions before I asked if I could speak.

"This doctor claims to know my sister but he doesn't know her at all. He doesn't even know she had a thriving piano business for over 20 years. He doesn't know she's been giving our mother her meals every day for years…helping our father; helping me most of my life when-ever I needed her. I have a car service waiting to take her to another hospital. I do not feel my sister is safe here. Please let me take my sister to a place she can get well."

Next they debated about the hospital transfer I had requested, while I watched her doctor eat a cookie, happily stating: "I'd never accept a patient from another hospital."

Finally, the judge spoke after a short recess.

After saying she found Leslie to be very ill: "I think it's in the best interests of the patient, that she be released to her sister to drive straight to St. Luke's Hospital."

Our lawyer suppressed a giggle of disbelief and began furiously writing a release. The court officer winked at me, smiled and whispered: "Good for you."

I mouthed a silent thank you to the judge who looked at my tears and silently mouthed: "Good luck," nodding up and down.

I went to tell Leslie she was free to leave.

"You mean I can go with you?"

"Yes!"

"Can I go tomorrow?"

"Get the fuck out of that bed now and get dressed."

"Okay."

In two seconds she slipped off the hospital gown and put her clothes on.

I had spoken with Bowtie the last week of August, to decide when to take Leslie to his hospital. He was vacationing somewhere and we spoke for a good 10 minutes. He sounded cheerful: "I'd be delighted to meet your sister," and confirmed as long as I brought her in through the ER, he would treat her. I wondered if he was wearing his bow tie on his vacation.

I asked Lewis if I should bring her to Bowtie because of the association with Stallion. "Yes, I'd take her to Bowtie, because he's already agreed," he said.

Both Lewis and Perlstein had already spoken with Bowtie to form a consensus.

When we got to St. Luke's, a resident shrink greeted me in the waiting room: "Let me see the discharge papers," in a cold, unsmiling manner.

"I don't have any."

"What do you mean? They had to give you papers."

"They just told us to leave."

"What? Without papers? I never heard of such a thing—they *had* to give you papers."

After two full hours of talking to Leslie and to me, they called me back in.

"You're not admitting her?"

"No—the judge felt she was okay to be released into society. We don't feel we need to admit her here."

I looked at Leslie lying across three chairs, on her dirty bag of clothes and her pink pillow, wearing thongs. My fears began escalating. I was more afraid this very moment than of confronting a gang in Sunset Park.

"I told you the judge only released her to me on the promise I'd bring her directly here—how can you do this? Dr. Bowtie told me he would accept her through the ER. She has no meds."

"Well, we just spoke with Dr. Bowtie and he said he never agreed to accept her. Didn't she get meds when the hospital discharged her?"

"What *do you mean* he said he never agreed to accept her? And no, they didn't give me any scripts. Where is she to go?"

"Can't she stay with you until you find a place?"

My brain started to burn.

I called Lewis. It was the first time Lewis heard me crying hysterically. It was the first time I can ever remember crying that way in my life. I cried all the time, but those were the regular easy tears that just fell. And it wasn't like that. This was new. I didn't know what I was feeling.

"Yes, it's crazy, it's totally crazy. I'll call Columbia," Lewis said.

I called Bowtie from the waiting room.

"I never agreed to this," he said in an angry tone.

"Dr. Bowtie—you told me at least four times if I brought her in through the ER that you would accept her."

"I never said that."

"Don't you remember telling Lewis and Dr. Perlstein? How can you say you never told all three of us? I have no meds."

"I do not believe Dr. Goodman, the resident psychiatrist at my hospital, did not give her scripts. I refuse to believe that."

Lewis called back in under five minutes:

"Nancy, take her to Columbia. Dr. M put her on the board—he's waiting."

As we were leaving, the resident handed me two scripts for Zyprexa and Synthroid, saying: "If you want to listen, I have something poignant to say. Leslie was asking for Klonipine and Ativan, two highly addictive meds, and I think you should know this because she isn't supposed to be on them, according to her doctor."

"So you're telling me my very ill sister is asking for meds *you think* she's not supposed to be on, while you're kicking us out of your hospital? You're right. That's very poignant." (Leslie *was* supposed to be on those meds. Melloman, the only shrink who made an improvement, had prescribed them months ago.)

I was now giving Leslie's history at Columbia, afraid they'd kick us out too. It was 9:00 p.m.

I glimpsed Leslie getting up from her seat and casually strolling through a corridor at a quickening pace until she began running.

"Leslie, where are you going?" as I began to run after her.

"I have to get out of here."

"No — stay." I tugged at her arm but I was no match for her strength.

"HELP!" was all I could yell as three angel security guards appeared out of nowhere, calmly steering Leslie back into the ER. They guarded her as she slid onto the floor, looking up at them like a child.

And that's how she got admitted. ◐●●

42

....

ONE MOVE

I had a dream that night:

Bram had conferenced me in, while he was talking to his financial advisor:

"So she stole the money out of my accounts and hid it somewhere?"

One of Bram's ex-wives had stolen money and he didn't know how to proceed. He was incredibly upset.

Next we were on the Brooklyn Bridge and Bram's arms were engulfing me. I said: "I don't want to talk about anything. I don't want to talk about your money problems or the carriage house or anything. Just kiss me. Let's just kiss."

I could feel the passion. We embraced with deep sensuous kisses. But soon he became focused on getting his money back and I broke away.

Then it became centuries earlier—there were no cars—the Brooklyn Bridge hadn't been built. People were using boats to navigate between Manhattan and Brooklyn.

I had two offers. I could go with Nathan and have no love but be at peace, or go with Bram and have love but no friendship.

I chose Bram but quickly retreated: "If I stay you can't love me—only if I leave you—then you'll love me."

I jumped in the boat. Nathan's enormous arms were rowing us away but water was seeping in. I had a mini hand-sized boat to bail out the water—it wasn't very effective.

I felt sick to leave Bram behind.

Leslie said: "Don't worry, you can always take a boat to Williamsburg to see him."

"Really—you think I'll see him again?"

"Sure—if you want to—he's not going anywhere."

Nathan was silently rowing us further and further away, not saying anything while hearing me speak of my love for Bram.

I've always wondered why some people choose the wrong path. Is it chemical? Are their brains chemically wired to be destructive?

Or is it environment?

Lewis says environment but when identical twins meet after being raised worlds apart there are tremendous similarities.

Leslie always says: "One thing changes everything."

Does one wrong move create a cascade of negative peptide linked receptor sites?

That day when Leslie met the dealer in the park, after Perlstein suggested she take that walk. If she hadn't walked on that day, or if he had been a lawyer, doctor, or anyone instead of a drug dealer, would she have said "Yes"?

Did saying "No" for over 12 years of celibacy tip the scales for her?

Lewis said when we try to correct for something, we usually overcorrect in one way or the other.

All I wanted was half of what my 'unusual' parents had—half would be tremendous.

I once told a potential date that I worked with my father and that my parents worked together for 30 years.

He reacted violently: "I'd probably kill my father if I worked with him."

43

....

LOSING MY RELIGION—AGAIN

I went to Friday night services, something my family never did. But I needed to expand and find positive anchors.

When I got to the temple the door wouldn't open. I spent 45 minutes driving from the east to the west side and there was no way I wasn't going in. I yanked and pulled until it finally gave way.

When I stepped inside, it was dark and stairs led to another locked door. Some people opened the first door and peered in. "Are you here for services?" I asked, suddenly feeling unsafe in this vestibule alone. They closed the door and walked away.

I came out to find some guy fiddling with the lock.

"Who are you?" I asked.

"Who are you I'd like to know—you just set the alarm off!"

"Oh—I'm trying to go to services—where is everybody?"

"They're having a party at the church on 49th—they came to pick up flyers. I'm the super—hope I can fix this lock. How'd you open it?"

A party sounded great, so I walked over to 49th and looked in. Everyone was looking back at me—they were facing some religious fixture and waved for me to come in. Rabbi Jill was singing—but it didn't sound happy.

Then some woman came up to the podium. I got to hear about her lice, holes in her feet, the Russians lining up the women and raping them repeatedly until they passed out. It was a Holocaust memorial service. When I met her in the ladies room afterward, I hugged her and she said: "Buy my book."

That night riding up in the elevator finally home with hot roasted turkey for my cuties:

"What are they gonna do when the next 200 banks cave?" said the elegant Robert Maxwell lookalike.

A surgeon still in scrubs said: "Why are they putting it in bonds?"

"Wait till they start jumping out of windows again—the FDIC can't guarantee when all this goes down," Elegant smiled.

My floor arrived: "I don't want to get off," I said to complete strangers.

"What should I put my money in? It's not safe in Chase?"

"Gold and silver," Elegant cautioned as the door closed.

I went on the Rabbi's website the next day to see who this Holocaust woman was. The website had an ad which asked if anyone had an apartment for the vice president of a wine company. I didn't think a VP would want a walk-up apartment in Sunset Park, but I emailed back.

Two days later a tall skinny fellow waltzed into my office to view the apartment. Upon seeing the light peach windowsills, he said: "I hate orange."

"What…who hates orange? I never heard anyone say they hate orange or say they hate any color. Besides you have orange on your head—you're a redhead."

Then he asked me if I liked wine.

"I've known too many alcoholics," I stated flatly.

"Oh—you're really missing out."

He started quoting some Italian and next some Spanish and finished with: "Do you think you could give me a boilerplate lease?"

"A what?"

"It's a Hollywood expression—you know I worked in Hollywood."

I told Morda I couldn't stop thinking of bedbugs and this guy.

I called Rabbi Jill: "Well Nancy—I really don't know him. Dan knows him—do you want Dan's number?"

"You don't know him? Who's Dan?"

"Dan's the president of the temple."

I called Dan: "Well Nancy—I really don't know him. He just walked into the temple one night and told me his story. He lives in a homeless shelter."

"*What???* He told me he's staying with friends who are divorcing, and needs his own space. No wonder he's refusing a credit check. You didn't screen this guy before advertising him to paying congregants?"

"I'll take him off the website immediately. I wasn't sure if he has mental problems…"

"He's a total con artist…you have no idea if anything he told you was true. I can't believe this." ●●

44

....

THE BLOB

Leslie's doctor stopped returning my calls when he found out I was against ECT. The social worker took over. She wanted a 'team' meeting.

I had these instantaneous images of people before I'd meet them. I pictured her a twisted 500-pound mess. *The Blob*. I wondered who abused her and how awful for her patients who had to suffer from her twisted junk.

The social worker *wasn't* 500 pounds; she was closer to 300 pounds.

While the doctor's eyes alternated between my cleavage and looking into space, the social worker commanded the meeting.

I told her I didn't want to discuss ECT with her. She continued to ask why.

"Because I don't want to discuss throwing electric currents and giving my sister a seizure with a social worker; I want an MD and I want it private. And if you don't understand this, then you shouldn't be in this profession."

They began talking to themselves about going to court—as if I would be intimidated.

That night I had a dream:

Leslie and I were home but the Blob was coming to get us. I started grab-bing pictures off the walls (as if they were the only thing of value)—pic-tures of my grandmother and her parents and some artwork.

I filled four enormously heavy garbage bags and slung them over my shoulder. I started the car, waiting for Leslie to come out. I ran back in-side. But Leslie wouldn't come out of the bathroom.

"Come ON Les—the Blob's coming!"

"Okay—I'm almost out."

Suddenly the Blob was coming out from under a sink—it was moving on the floor toward another door—Leslie was inside.

"LES!"

"Nan, HELP! THE BLOB IS IN HERE."

I felt true fear—a horrible wave of loss if Leslie would be swallowed by it. I frantically thought how I could rescue her...

But her blood-curdling scream woke me up.

I had to resign myself and face it—I lost Leslie.

She would never get going fast enough to outrun whatever was in her brain that was stealing her out of my life. ●●

45

....

HEALTHY AS AN OX

I went to another psychic. She told me:

"Bram's going down even more—and you're not. I don't know why he's with his ex—he never loved her. He's crazy about you. *He's crazzzy about you!* Does he have a brother or a best friend?"

"Both."

"Is one of them a little bit weird?"

"Both."

"His family's a bit off. I feel he has problems with his father. They don't get along. All families are weird but his is very difficult—he has sisters?"

"Yes, two."

"I don't know…he can't escape these people surrounding him. He can't get out—it's like he's manipulated by everyone and thinks it's love. *Ooooh*—wait—you're supposed to be together. Why is his ex still there? Does she have money?"

"He has money."

"Well I don't know how, but she controls it. He's got guilt—I don't know what that's all about but it's his guilt that binds him. He needs you to tell him what to do or he's going to spend the rest of his life under her control—this is his wound—he doesn't stand up for himself."

"He's afraid he'll lose his kids," I responded.

"It's in his head. He's living in this illusion. But he wants to be with you—he really does. I can tell you that. I see a lot of pain. He knows the mask has to come off and he's frightened. Oh—things will change—I see him wanting to be the man for you.

But I need to get away from this right now. Let's move on…let's do health. What's wrong with your eyes? Aren't they okay? Maybe you've just been crying. *Oooh,* I'm getting a past life…you were a man in England" (she starts giggling) "people were making fun of you—you had something wrong with your shoulder, like a hunchback…I know your mother is very ill, and I'm sorry but I don't think your father is going to be around very long either."

"What? My dad's as healthy as an ox—he's just crazy."

"I don't think so. I see something's going on. *He doesn't have long.*" ◕-●

46

....

TUNA FISH

"Nancy, your mom's on the phone." Morda interrupted my exam, which was highly unusual and even moreso because my mom knew not to bother me at work.

"Daddy just dropped a plate."

"Did he have a seizure, a stroke?"

"I don't know—he was bringing me lunch and he just dropped a plate of tuna in the hallway."

"What's he doing now?"

"I don't know—he's very confused."

"Is he mumbling again?"

"Yes."

I had called my mother at midnight to say goodnight and heard him mumbling in the background. I asked if she thought he'd had a stroke, assuming it was just more of his rambling nonsense.

I asked my new optician—Mr. Wu—to drive because I didn't trust myself.

On the ride, an agonizing feeling caught me by surprise—a deep horror almost. It never occurred to me my dad wasn't going to be around many more years to drive me crazy.

I thought of his legs—they'd gotten too skinny—he lost too much weight. The look on his face was different—I felt incredibly sad for some loss I couldn't face and for *his loss*—his life suffering.

When I got to my folks I cautiously peered into the hallway, not wanting to step on the tuna. I saw a plate and fork on the floor, but no tuna.

"Where's the tuna fish?"

My dad was sitting upright on the edge of the bed, looking extremely anxious. I put the plate and fork in the sink, still wondering if the tuna fell elsewhere. I quickly washed the floor where the invisible tuna would have been.

"What hospital should we go to?" I asked my mom.

"Take him to South Nassau."

My father resisted.

"Get dressed right now. You're not dying on me," I commanded.

"Come on Lenny, you could have had a stroke," my mom said, biting her cuticles.

He finally got ready. Mr. Wu was sitting in the kitchen. My father had trouble walking so Mr. Wu practically carried him into the back seat.

"Mom, don't worry. I'll bring him back."

"Okay Nan—you promise?"

For the first 10 minutes Mr. Wu kept making different turns because I couldn't decide where to direct him.

"We're going to Columbia," not wanting to take any chances.

"No, Nan—I don't want to go there. South Nassau," my dad's stubbornness still intact.

I instructed Mr. Wu how to get to the city from our house.

We finally arrived at the ER. After 45 minutes of questions they let him sit on a bed.

The resident came over and showed him her pen.

"What's this?" she asked.

"It's a slick."

"And what's this?" pointing to her glasses.

"Keys," with his hands open, as if everyone knew that.

It was my dad's voice—the best voice I've ever heard—saying all the wrong things. The way he said these words sounded right to him, which was the scary part. Then it got worse.

Pointing to his mouth: "My foam rolws," he said to me over and over again. He was distraught and kept touching his chin and mouth. I told him I knew what he meant—his foam was his mouth and rolws meant words.

He was also worried about shaving because stubble was appearing. I also got he was worried about who was going to take the mail in. He began to worry about all of his responsibilities, because my mom was so ill. I reassured him I'd take care of everything. Who was going to take care of my mom though?

I called Singh. He said he would sleep over the house and give my mom her meds. When Bram had called a car service to take me to his first rehab — Singh was the driver. He became my driver whenever my family had a crisis. He had become an integral part of managing my folks.

I called Singh in between doctor appearances:

"Singh — did you give her the Verapamil?"

"What?"

"Verapamil — V–E–R–A–P–A–M–I–L."

"Yes Nancy — I gave her Benadryl."

"No Singh — Verapamil!"

We went through this 10 times but the Indian accent has a hard time with 'V.'

"Singh — V–V–V."

"Yes Nancy — I give her B…"

I called my cat-loving neighbor, who said he'd go over. When he got to the house he called: "Now what am I supposed to give her? I see Ambien… I can't find the Verapamil."

My dad started talking about his sister: "She plays taxes every day with her yankles." That meant she plays tennis every day with her ankles. She had bad ankles.

Some of his sentences came out normal, followed by: "I have weeds in my ass. Check the amount of wop in there." Which meant the urine bag.

One of the doctors asked him if knew where he was and I gently hinted it was his alma mater.

He responded: "Portawetical."

While still in the ER, he had a CT scan. When the tech left the room—I had to know—I peeked in when no one was watching.

And then I saw it—an enormous mass in his left temporal lobe.

Silent Gulp.

At 3:00 a.m. they sent us to get an MRI.

Two big men tried to stuff my dad's head into the MRI grating. "You can't do that—you can't bend his neck—it doesn't bend," as I ran toward him.

They finally realized my dad's neck was a piece of steel. "Look we have to lift him up diagonally and slide him in," as I instructed them. The three of us raised my dad up and angled him down onto it. Then I put my fingers under his neck and did the best traction of my life. The problem now was his huge nose. I did more neck traction. He finally fit.

After the MRI, one of the techs was bullying him—rushing him, not giving a damn if he hurt him. But what creeped me out was his silence. It was the spookiest thing.

I said: "Say something—you can talk."

"What am I supposed to say?" he said ominously.

It was now late Tuesday and we were still in the ER. I thought Leslie should know. The social worker agreed and encouraged me to come over. This was no easy thing. Every time I had to enter a locked unit I became tense, wondering what objects they'd confiscate and how we'd be monitored.

I had no reserve left—I was on thin ice ready to fall through.

But when I arrived—three women came into the hall: A social worker, an administrator, and the head nurse. "I decided Leslie is not in the condition to know about her father," the nurse said.

Her hand was in her pocket like Bogart in *The Caine Mutiny* and she was clanking away with her keys instead of ball bearings. The more she talked, the more they clanked and she wouldn't let go of them.

"Okay, so I was told to come here, and now you're not letting me tell my own sister that our father might need brain surgery."

Ignoring me, the administrative woman asked: "Do you know his prognosis?" as if it weren't my father, as if it weren't my father who I loved and was trying not to cry about.

"I don't care to discuss that with you," was all I said.

"Leslie is an extremely fragile human being and is going to need *a lot* of support wherever she winds up," clanking away.

"Is that what you do? You think and act like she's so fragile that you don't expect strength from her?"

(I thought of Perlstein: **"You act like *she's going to get well* and *make this known to her.*"**)

"Okay, so I can blame all of you if our father dies, that you didn't let me tell my sister."

By Wednesday my dad was in the Neuro unit a floor below Leslie with the friendliest residents on staff. They were thrilled to get a brain tumor. "You wanna see it?" they asked me.

"Okay," putting on the best show I could. So while they smiled at their advanced technology, I wondered how they were going to get that thing out of my dad's brain.

Surgery was scheduled for Friday until the surgeon saw the MRI and moved it up a day. My dad needed a full-body MRI before the surgery.

After we came to a new floor for the MRI, he startled me with perfect speech: "What do you think they think I have?"

"What do *you* think they think?" letting him lead, conveying he knew better than I.

"Maybe it's a brain tumor."

"Well—maybe but they're not sure."

"So what do we do if it is?"

"What do you *want* to do?" still letting him be in control.

"We take care of it."

"That's right, that's what we're gonna do," and I kissed him.

After the test, I didn't know why it was taking so long to release us. Then the radiologist happened to catch me in the hallway: "Do you have any information on your dad's kidneys?"

"He only has one—congenital, born that way."

"Oh God, we were spending an hour trying to figure it out."

Sure, don't ask — just let my dad stay in your unit all this time a nervous wreck, I thought.

Singh left my mom to pick me up. Since Monday she had been calling every hour. Sometimes she called wondering where Singh was only to be told he was napping in the living room, as I had just woken him up trying to find him.

"Well he should tell me if he's going to nap in the living room, how do I know?"

The problem was she couldn't understand a thing he said. I looked at my mom. I looked at Singh.

"Mom — maybe you should come into the city with me."

"How?"

"Singh can put you in the car."

My mother hadn't been out of the house in two years. I found out later that the home visiting doctor had told her not to go outside. What would be the reason anyone would discourage a person from getting fresh air? So he could have continued home visits?

"Yes Sandra — I carry you." Singh once lifted a treadmill out of my house. He and my mother had developed an unusual relationship I still don't understand. They loved each other. When he would drop me off, he would say: "Sandra, you want massage?" And he would massage her legs and feet for 20 minutes. Then he would heat up Italian food and bring it to her in bed. He would insist she eat.

Afterwards he would pick her up and turn her body so it faced my dad.

Her back was curved out and she was more comfortable on her right side but Singh would insist she lie on her left to be closer to my dad.

We rolled her to the top of the stairs in a tiny walker that has the seat attached for when you tire. I had bought it long ago but it remained in the living room never used. I fit pants and a jacket on her—clothes she hadn't worn in two years either. She wore her big fluffy mop slippers—the only things that didn't kill her feet.

I stood there for at least five minutes figuring out all the reasons to take her and all the reasons not to. But nothing made any sense lately so I just went with it. Singh picked her up like a baby while I ran out to his car and opened the back door. He came down the stairs briskly with my mother in a panic.

I raced back into the house and took all the meds I saw (not knowing which I'd need). I grabbed three nightgowns, some underwear, and boxes of cookies.

Off we were on a ride to Manhattan at 4:00 a.m. The first time she breathed outside air in two years. My mom didn't close her eyes once. She had a look of bewilderment on her face.

"Mom—isn't this incredible? You're coming to the city. You're going to see my apartment for the first time. You're going to see Daisy, Samson, and Bisqui."

"I don't know...I can't believe it. We're really going into the city? *Daisy ... Wow.*" ◖◗

47

....

VOODOO WOMEN

I got back to the hospital at 7:00 a.m. I asked the staff if my father had gone to the bathroom. "You see I'm busy," one said while she was eating potato chips.

I held him up, as his balance was gone while we walked very slowly to the bathroom. He dropped down onto the low seat with a thud, while I held on. After a while he stood up with his legs shaking and pointed into the seat. He mumbled a terrible sound. He had lost all speech in the past several hours.

There was anguish on his face from his loss of dignity. He kept pointing. I looked into the bowl and saw three enormous plops. I felt unbelievably upset my dad was heading into brain surgery with three big plops in him. How many times I've had worse than three big plops—thanking God for that toilet.

I thought of my blind roommate when I had my liver surgery—she was crying hysterically because no one came after she yelled for half an hour. She finally wet the bed.

Seeing a blind person crying when they can't see everyone watching them—it doesn't get much worse, yet—it was impossible not to think of Deanna at every turn: *Deanna—your rash because the staff never cleaned you—Daddy having brain surgery in only three days, and you waiting an entire year not being able to breath—then finally your life saving chance for surgery and…*

When we reached the OR, he let go of the tight grip we held under his sheet, not wanting anyone to see our silent bond. He couldn't even mumble by then. But the female orderly knew:

"He was holding your hand tight, right? That's the way I am with my dad."

I went home to shower and give my cats their 12:00 p.m. insulin. As I was heading back to the hospital I turned my cell back on. There was a text: "Hi Nan—are you okay? Love, me."

"Who is this?" I texted back only realizing a second later. "Oh—my dad just had brain surgery and I'm going back to the hospital."

"Nan—it's me—Bram. I'm sorry about your dad. I hope he's okay. And your birthday is June 2nd."

The last time we'd had dinner almost a year ago, he'd mentioned every single month except mine when I'd asked if he remembered. He went through 11 months and never said June.

How was he texting me on the exact day my father had brain surgery? And why didn't he call as soon as he heard?

I got another text later: "Did I not say the right thing?" he asked.

"Just to be sure it's you, what did we see at Miraval?"

"We saw cows and a bull and we made a rock sculpture," he texted.

Okay so it was him. *But why the texting?* I couldn't afford to lose it— my hurt was too deep from him and my mom needed me terribly. I had to deal with brain surgeons and voodoo women.

I shut my phone off.

The surgery took over five hours. I spent most of it trying to avoid strangers who wanted to talk about 'loved ones' they didn't care about.

They finally let me see him in recovery. *He looked great.* No swelling. Hardly anything except a tiny bandage by the tinier incision. (I thought of Deanna again and the awful descriptions of her useless biopsy.)

The surgeon had warned me it would take several days for him to speak but there was a huge improvement immediately. Although some words were out of reach, he could speak full sentences.

When his assigned male nurse came over to do some testing, my dad said: "You're going to be my friend?"

His direct cool voice saying it straight.

Later on a neurologist came by. He spoke to my dad for five minutes. Then he told me: "Your dad is extremely depressed and if we don't treat his depression he's not going to survive the cancer." Then he smiled and walked away.

I stayed over that night afraid to leave him. I hired someone to give my cats their insulin and help my mom.

We did an MRI the very next day. They didn't give him a break. He was so nervous they had to sedate him. I instructed them how to slide him in and not injure his neck. His nose still came out squished and bleeding.

Bram texted right after: "What's going on with your dad? I miss talking—I don't know what to do."

Later that evening my dad was switched to a private room back in the same Neuro unit. No nurse was assigned to him. He was completely incoherent, distraught, and vulnerable.

I went to the head nurse: "How can they put my father in a private room with no nurse?"

"Well, they wouldn't have put him there if it wasn't okay and we'll check on him—once an hour."

Okay, so he'll die from falling.

I made many phone calls but nothing could be done. I went home and gave in—all composure lost—I hadn't slept for three days.

I got a call at 10:00 p.m. from a psychiatrist:

"I put your dad back in a four-person. He's delirious. Who ordered that private room?"

He said he'd check on my dad every day from then on. I cried with my mom from relief—that he would be safe.

The next day the surgeon came to see me: "It wasn't a cyst like I told you. It's a glioma—the Teddy Kennedy kind."

"How long?" I asked.

"Well it depends, but 2 to 11 months…closer to 2."

"Should we have done the surgery?" I wanted to know.

"Well, you wouldn't have been able to talk to him and he'd have been gone in a month."

Two months. *Two months? Only two months to be with my dad?* The man I screamed at all those times—thinking he was just being nuts and could stop. I cannot describe what I felt in words. It was just deep, weighty, and raw.

I also felt a tremendous burden lifted—*my dad wasn't nuts?* Everything started to make sense now.

But I knew my dad wouldn't want to know what he had. If he had been younger maybe. Before Deanna got sick. Before his wife couldn't walk. Before his other daughter became a coke addict. Maybe then he'd want to know.

I kept the cyst story going: "Yeah Dad, just a cyst they had to drain."

I kept it going for my mom too—she had this look I had only seen once before, when Deanna got sick.

This was worse though. ●●

48

....

FLOATING

My next decision was to do acute rehab or longer term. I opted for acute to get him home sooner. An ambulette was called to take him to Mount Sinai—two guys playing loud rock music showed up.

I was holding my dad's head, trying to keep it still and lost track of time. I realized it was taking too long to go across Central Park. I looked out—we were heading onto 34th Street.

My dad was in excruciating pain—his head bobbing constantly.

"What are you doing on 34th Street? Mt. Sinai is on 101st…10 minutes away."

"Well this is what the GPS says," the driver shouted over the music.

"What are you talking about—where are you going, seriously?"

"It says it's in Queens, you know there are a lot of Mount Sinais," he said.

"What are you kidding me—what is wrong with you—turn up Madison right now before you miss it. How do you not know where you're going with someone so ill?"

Next a woman came through the speaker: "Where the hell are you? I told you how to go—you should have been here half an hour ago."

The very next day my dad's speech was impeccable, conveying exactly how he felt—as I heard when I approached his room:

"YOU FUCKIN' ASSHOLE—YOU LOUSY SON OF A BITCH, GET THE FUCK OUT OF HERE…"

I peeked in to see it was him: *"NANCYYYYYY—NANCYYYYYY—* COME BACK!"

I ran to one of his doctors. This was not normal, not my father. My parents were refined. The doctor said the cursing was a side effect from the steroids he needed to stop his brain from swelling.

I grew up with a father whose only curse words were: "Bastard" and "Creep."

My mom only cursed when my dad impressed her with something, saying: "He's a fuckin' genius."

Yet no one would believe his genuine language was pristine, because his curses now sounded so natural.

That night and every night hence we would repeat the same dialog: "You're leaving and you're never coming back—you lousy bitch—"

"Dad—please—I need you—I love you—just give me a kiss."

"Okay—now get the fuck out of here and shut off the light. What time are you coming tomorrow? You'll never come."

For some reason the nurses and interns giggled and never got upset. They would apologize to me for their laughter, but I couldn't have been more grateful for how much they liked a man who only cursed them.

One of the youngest residents suggested a palliative care team to help me negotiate with the uncooperative senior doctors. This included a female Rabbi, a resident psychiatrist, and another intern. The resident psychiatrist was everything the head shrink wasn't. He cared.

One day he said: "I've never seen this before."

"Seen what?"

"I've never seen a family member care so much for their parent. You usually don't see this. Most people don't care."

"I don't know what you're talking about. I'd rather be with my dad than anywhere else."

"Well, how'd you get to be this way?"

"What do you mean?"

"What made you able to handle this? Most people can't."

"Him. Them. My folks are the greatest people."

On another day, a woman who had an ill family member came over to me. She was very well-coiffed, all designer, her blond hair immaculate.

"I've been watching you and I think you're amazing."

"What do you mean?"

"I just think you're amazing."

Then she disappeared into the room she always visited.

One nurse unexpectedly cornered me in the kitchenette with a desperate voice: "How can I get my kids to love me the way you love your dad and take care of me like you do?"

"Always be true to them."

She nodded—slowly taking it in. She saw my routine every day: the cut-up pizza in the microwave, the Ben and Jerry's pops, bothering them all for extra urine pads, sheets, and towels. I'd walk him to his bathroom only a few steps from his bed, five to six times every day. No one ever came to change him. She feared no one would for her.

The staff would secretly pass me his meds—he would only take them from me. I bribed him with ice cream.

After I'd get a couple of pizza bites in him, we'd watch the Yankee game all curled up—him in his bed and me in the chairs next to him with sheets over me. I held his forearm. The Yankees and Ben and Jerry's saved us.

It was intuitive to me to protect my parents. To help them preserve their dignity. To love them as they had always loved me. Was it so rare?

One day I came in to find my father strapped naked to a wheelchair. They had decided to give him a shower like that against his will.

"Look what they did to me," with a look I need to forget.

I believe that's the day that changed my father's fate.

The next day he braved the mirror for the first time since his surgery.

"I look like such a schmuck," he said about himself.

Several times a day he would say: "I'm going on a trip. I'm spinning and spinning and don't you see that spinning up towards the ceiling?"

"Can I go on the trip with you?"

"No you can't come and I've already started my trip."

"Is it okay? Where are you going?"

"I don't know but I'm floating."

"Can you float above me and not leave me?"

"Yes maybe I can do that, I'll have to see."

"Is there any way you can go on the trip in a year?"

"I know you love me a lot, but my trip has already started."

My father didn't want to go on this trip. We both knew what it meant. That's why it was so bad when the Yankees weren't on to distract him. He'd begin worrying about this 'trip.'

I would get periodic texts from Bram asking me how things were going:

"I think about you every day—I can't stop thinking about you. Another day without you. What do you want? What should we do?"

I texted: "Don't think right now—just think hug—it's all I need."

"Okay—that sounds good."

On my birthday he wrote: "Hey Nan, Happy Birthday! When's a good time to call?"

It's the first time I phased him out. I wanted to see him badly but the fact he didn't run to hold me—after hearing my dad had brain surgery—I had to block it out. It was safer keeping him in the dark where he wanted to be.

I preferred to be with a man who yelled: "FUCK YOU—I HATE YOU—YOU STINK—GET THE HELL OUT OF HERE AND WHEN ARE YOU COMING BACK?"

Like a little kid whose parents go away and he's too hurt when they return and has no say when they'll leave again. No control. The staff let me stay after hours but I didn't want to abuse the privilege. I was happier to have him curse me than not be able to talk at all.

We always got over it and said "I love you" at least three times before I left each night.

Getting my dad home is something I don't like to think about. I chose Singh rather than an ambulette. I got an evening discharge to avoid rush hour traffic.

My dad resisted. He kept his body so rigid, that Singh and I had to squish him into the car. On the 59th Street Bridge I feared he would open a back door and jump out.

When we finally got home my dad sank to the ground. My dad was one of those comedians even when it wasn't funny. When Singh tried to carry him, my dad just sank further down into the driveway. He wouldn't let Singh carry him. So Singh lifted him straight up and as they entered the house Singh was nine feet tall and had to crouch down so my dad wouldn't hit the ceiling.

Later on Singh said: "Nancy your father very fat, very heavy."

"Singh—he weighs only 98 pounds now."

"Oh my God Nancy—your father is so strong." ●●

49

....

HOME AT LAST

It was now June 8th and both my parents were back home in their bed—together. My three remaining cats were with us too. Every day I had to reassure both my parents I wouldn't leave.

I had hired a patient of mine who was a home attendant, Ernestine. The first day she arrived was great and the second day too. She told me God sent me to her because the bills were piling up and she had little work. But by the third day the new deal was laid upon me fast:

"Nancy, food is very expensive and I know I said I'd bring my own but I really need you to pay for it. And *do you mind* if I take that suitcase, microwave, toaster oven, and *do you mind* not doing the laundry after a certain hour?"

Each day was a new request: "Nancy—I'm afraid to ask you this—but *do you think* you could bring the refrigerator inside from the garage— cause it's cold in there."

Never once had Leslie complained about this refrigerator, generating a whole new respect for Leslie. Besides, it was an extra fridge—she was welcome to use the one inside that we all used.

I had thrown out my dad's gym bag. It took a lot for me to part with it. I looked at it for several days debating what to do. I felt great relief when I packed it deep in the garbage.

The following day I saw it back in the kitchen.

"Ernestine — that's my father's bag — you don't want it."

"I can use it." Her high voice would slip into baritone when she forgot the facade.

After a while she stopped getting up at night to help my dad. What was I paying her for?

One day she was sitting right in-between them, like a walrus separating their bodies to watch a movie. My parents looked distraught. I took a look, never expecting to see *One Flew Over The Cuckoo's Nest*. My father had a clear view of it.

"Turn that off right now. Do not watch movies like that with my father."

Was she vicious?

That evening when she was giving him ice cream *in bed*, she said: "Don't you want to get in your own bed?"

"Don't do that, don't play games with his mind and make him more confused than he is."

How was I going to manage without her? She knew how to do the bathroom. Even if her voice skipped octaves depending on her mood, she could lift him if he fell.

Lewis said I must insist on 24-hour care from hospice and that four hours wasn't legal. When the hospice manager came and saw Ernestine sleeping midafternoon, they agreed. But if Ernestine was awful, the hospice was worse.

Who knew that 'nurse practitioner' didn't mean nurse? It's an aide with a nurse label in front of it. So they slept, studied, and let my parents go unattended. They all asked: *"Who's the patient?"* when they saw my folks in bed.

There was one aide who came unannounced one day and flashed a huge smile, finding himself quite handsome. Even if he was mostly on his laptop, he would gently guide my mother to the bathroom without hesitation. He helped with her morning meds. He began to bring her food even though *she* wasn't the patient.

I was able to take catnaps with him around, but always with my door wide open.

We decided maybe I could go to work one day if he was watching them, so Morda scheduled a full day of patients. But my dad got a fierce grip on my hand and repeatedly shouted: *"DON'T GO!"*

He was emaciated but his strength was enormous. I didn't go. It wasn't a question.

I made it to the office three times in a four-month period. Morda said: "They're all waiting for you. They don't want to go anywhere else. They feel really bad, you know, about your dad and what you're going through."

"Do you think we'll be alright?" I asked, pretty worried about income.

"Wait, just wait till you see the list of people I've got."

Since my dad had dropped the plate, somehow I had put in $170K to keep the practice going—taxes, salaries, the building needed the back wall redone, rent, their house. It was all adding up quickly. With no money coming in and what I'd lost with Bram, I wondered how we'd survive.

Then my mom began to complain about her feet and her stomach. It was sudden and then relentless. I found it strange she would complain when my dad was so ill. I finally got two home care agencies to come. One doctor came twice within a two-week period.

"Please make sure she doesn't have pneumonia. She almost died from it twice," I said.

While my mother began a new hopeful regimen of in-home care, my father started going down fast. Within two weeks there was a drastic change. He stopped eating the Italian ziti we ordered every night, and wanted only ice cream and candy. I gave him whatever he wanted whenever he asked. He went through gallons of ice cream. I sent Singh to different supermarkets if they were out of cherry vanilla.

As my father began to get sicker, my mother's complaints increased. I assumed it was a way for her not to focus on losing him. A kind of strategy of self-absorption she never showed before.

I tried getting her to focus on a new life with me; all the things we were going to do. The first thing was getting the dog she always wanted—a Wire Fox Terrier. The next thing was getting her smile back—some new teeth. Since Singh had brought her to my apartment, we realized she could go anywhere. I told her she had to hang around until I met 'HIM.' She promised she'd stick around.

I started to think about the day it all began. *Where was that tuna fish?* I got a shiver.

There was never any tuna fish. That's why he dropped the plate.

He looked down and saw he was just bringing her a fork without the meal. I imagined the plate falling out of his hands because he couldn't figure it out. This was a brain who always sat at the kitchen table doing word puzzles, figuring out the riddle. The strategic ball player, never missing a shot. The musician—playing his sax, flute, and piano, as the band leader up in the Catskills. The Blackjack ace—doubling down. The physics major who knew how things worked. Bringing his wife all of her meals and pills—handling everything. Managing the check book just one day before.

I closed my eyes and exhaled, remembering his mumbling and sitting with impeccable posture on the edge of his bed, when I asked where the tuna was—not understanding the look of fear in his eyes.

Now I understood. 👓

50

....

CRASHING

By the end of June my father's skin had a pallor I hadn't seen before. Then one day I walked in and saw a corpse… still alive. It had taken only 24 hours. I almost didn't recognize him. Everything changed. My mother couldn't see him because she remained on her right side facing away.

The last two days were excruciating because he was delirious and kept yelling: **"Get out of here!!!"**

Singh said he was talking to the death people — that my father was telling the *bad* death people to leave because the *nice* death people weren't there yet. I only left his side to go to the bathroom.

The Rabbi and social worker came. I needed the Rabbi to know this was different. This was devastating.

"Rabbi, this isn't just someone dying. This is about two people who have a very rare love."

When he said: "Then we take the body," I began crying.

"I'm sorry Nancy, I'm sorry."

Did he think we were taking out the garbage?

"Can you say 'my dad'? Please don't say 'The Body.'"

The social worker had thyroid eyes and was so manic she looked like she was about to hyperventilate: "Do you need any medication, tranquilizers or prescriptions?"

"What? Don't ask me that; that makes a person feel weak."

"I have to ask you *that*. That's part of my job."

"I've never seen this before," she said. (*On no, what is it this time — what is the thing that no one's seen before?*)

"I've never seen two people in the same bed when someone's…you know. Why are they in the same bed?"

"What are you talking about? It's *their* bed—it's *his* bed—they *want* to be there."

She began arguing.

"I'm not moving him out of his own bed. This is his house. I'm not doing it," I said.

Her eyes locked into mine: "His soul is going to leave his body."

I felt some horrible thing aside from death was going to happen. I didn't want my dad to be all alone in a crummy tiny hospital bed against the wall. I wanted him to feel like the King who was leaving his domain and not to feel worse. I hate when people take away a person's power just because that person can't stop them.

Then one morning I knew. I didn't need a social worker to scare me. I just knew my mom would be better off in my bed—not hearing him in such pain.

The hospice didn't tell me the correct dose of morphine. *What were they worried about? That I was going to kill a dying man? They had to be careful he stayed in horrific pain lest I use even a little more?*

I had a secret stash of Ambien and Oxycodone my mom had stored up for years making me promise never to let her die in pain. But I wasn't able to do it. I was worried it would wind up in my cats' water. I hid it high on a shelf in the bathroom.

Perlstein kept saying: *"Comfort and dignity."* But it was neither.

When I called the hotline about the morphine, the nurse said: "That's way too low a dose. He needs double or triple, but I have to get permission."

Oh sure right, I'll wait—I ran to the fridge and took triple the amount and put it under his tongue out of eyesight of the aide.

Within seconds my dad's moans lowered. I held my dad, who sounded like an elevator crashing down each floor. I felt his body crash down in brutal force while he moaned deeply and fearfully.

I whispered in his ear:

"I'm right here. I'll never leave you. We're going together each of us—a piece stays here and a piece goes there and you'll get through this. Don't be scared I'm never leaving you. I love you Dad. Just stay around me, don't leave me either."

I had put restrictions on my father: "You can't die until after July 4th."

It was July 8th.

I never heard his last breath, but I felt it because I was holding him so tightly. His pulse continued and I continued to look for it until it stopped by his carotid. But I wasn't sure until Singh came. The aide wasn't sure either.

Singh walked in and said: "Nancy, your father died."

Singh sat on the hospital bed in a yoga position.

"Singh, please stay with him, don't leave him alone."

"Nancy, it's same for us—we're not allowed to leave them. Don't worry, I stay with your father."

I didn't know how to tell my mom. I avoided it for about an hour. When I went into my room, all my cats were surrounding her like a shield.

"Mom, Daddy's at peace now. He's not in pain anymore."

"Uh-oh," with her fingers in her mouth and her eyebrows raised.

She sat up.

"Come on Mom, you promised you're gonna be with me for at least another two years. I can't live without you. I just won't be able to."

"I don't know if I can."

"But you promised. I need you. I really, really won't be able to do this."

"Okay—I'll try—I just don't know."

I don't think her look ever changed from that day.

I went into the living room because people started gathering. The hospice coordinator came and asked me what time I wanted to make it. She said I was allowed to 'call the time' because it doesn't really need to be exact. I knew when his last breath was—*but was that the real time if his heart was still beating?*

I said: "Make it 8:16," to match my charge card expiration date so I'd never forget.

Then the funeral home came—two men in black. I knew not to look when they took him, and stayed in the living room.

The thyroid social worker came and said: "I'm going to open a window to free his soul."

One of the religious men in black started to fill out paperwork and said: "It's Mr. Leonard Glassman?"

"Dr. Leonard Glassman," I said.

"This is *DR. LEONARD GLASSMAN? I know him.*"

How could this guy possibly know my dad?

Turns out these guys the Rabbi recommended were from Borough Park and did know my father. But more than that, they spoke of him as if he were still alive, which was crucial to keeping me above water.

They probably didn't realize how they were speaking of him in the present tense, but it made all the difference to me.

I got a call later on from a different Rabbi who actually owned the funeral home: "You know Nancy, everyone here knows your dad and they said when people didn't have money, your father would give them glasses for free."

The reverence in his voice caught me off guard.

I had put together a racquet, silk bathrobe, and a King from a deck of cards, wanting my father to be comfortable and regal—knowing he'd never want to be in a suit and tie. I also had a picture of his three girls to put on his chest.

In the back of my mind I hoped they weren't doing that weird sack thing—*what did they call it?* Uchss—a shroud. It has an ominous ring for me—where they bury the person naked in a sack—I didn't want to know. I wanted to picture my dad in his blue striped robe. But these guys looked like the shroud type—maybe even beyond Orthodox—I had no idea how religious they were.

Then I went into their bedroom.

I didn't know how my mom would come back into this room without him being in it. I moved the unused rental bed across the room, until I could get rid of it. I put their own bed against a different wall so it changed the entire look of the room. I didn't know if this was a good or bad thing.

It was completely unlike her previous layout, taking the chance that a more confusing *new* layout was easier than an old familiar (yet frightening) one absent her Lenny.

Because that's the look she had—a kind of terror. They had never spent more than four days apart their entire marriage.

I remember my neighbor dying very young from asthma and his wife saying: "That bed." She hated sleeping alone in the bed she had shared with her husband.

Strategically now the bed was right next to the bathroom a few feet away, as opposed to the 30 paces she needed to walk before—less chance for a fall. I had no one close enough to talk about this to. She was the one I always spoke to.

At about 5:00 a.m. I went to figure out what I would wear to my dad's funeral. I had a thin summery skirt from years before I never wore. It was perfect. It was in the pile to be donated. I also had $300 sandals. I thought my dad would be proud.

The cemetery was in Westchester—somewhere my dad's family had picked. My aunt didn't shut up the entire ride and I couldn't do anything to silence her. My mother didn't want her sister to fly in and unfortunately I encouraged it.

After the Rabbi spoke, we had arranged that I could have some privacy with my dad. Morda guided my aunt away but my aunt refused—she didn't want to be guided away—she wanted to be in on anything and everything.

Finally the Rabbi and I were alone. I asked the Rabbi to ask the spirits to keep my father around my mom and me and not to leave us until we could join him.

I knelt down closer to my dad again and the Rabbi knelt down too as he had the entire time I was sitting on the grass. "I'm sorry Dad," I must have said 20 times.

I couldn't tell the Rabbi how I always screamed at my dad. The Rabbi must have thought I was sorry about what my dad went through. But I was apologizing over and over again not being able to forgive myself: *"I'm sorry Dad."*

On the ride home, we stopped off at my apartment in the city to use the bathroom and my aunt's mouth ran nonstop:

"I hate you, you're so thin. *So* you got a bed—a new bed—*just* for your mom? And a new TV? What's with the bags? I didn't know this was a New York thing now. *Okay*, so how much does a place like this cost?"

I sat silently as her questions fell over me. There was not a moment where her mouth was closed. She put down everyone I loved.

"Well, your mom could *never* be like your dad. Your dad was like a saint, you know. Grandma had a lot of boyfriends, *a lot*. She was gorgeous. Both she and your mom were stunning. Why aren't you married?"

"Morda," was all I could say.

"Nancy needs us to be quiet now," Morda snapped.

And that shut her up until we dropped her off. 👓

51

···············

THE WINDOW

Soon as I got home I went to hug my mom: "Why is her head tilted back like that?"

The aide was asleep under the covers on the rental bed, with his back to my mom. He quickly sat up: "She said she likes it like that."

"What? She doesn't like it like that, she's delirious… Mom??—*MOM! CAN YOU HEAR ME?*"

No response.

I felt her forehead and immediately ran to put alcohol on it. Singh came in. "Singh! 911!"

"Yes Nancy—911!"

I grabbed a thermometer after calling 911 and thought it was broken when it read 104. When the EMT came he got 105.

"Let's go to South Nassau," thinking it's the best of the worst.

When we got to the ER they threw her on an ice bed with an ice body bag around her which looked like a float filled with ice. They also put individual ice packs all over key body parts and kept moving them around.

While my mom lay fighting for her life, the head nurse came in and started yelling at the staff:

"I told you to keep changing the packs. What are you doing?"

She started rearranging the ice packs—moving with lightning speed. I felt relieved she was yelling and caring.

I pulled the head nurse aside: "I just got back from my dad's funeral; please don't let my mom die."

"I got it," was all she said giving me back the straight stare.

I had to give insulin to Daisy and Samson. I felt safe to leave with her in charge. This was an unimportant hospital where unimportant people died but with her fever, Columbia was too far for my mom.

I went back the next day to find my mother in a regular room shivering. I went to the head nurse:

"My mom has pneumonia, is shivering, and turning blue. She needs to be in ICU—she can't breathe."

"She doesn't have pneumonia. And she ran a fever again so she needs the ice bag."

For the next two hours I fought with the staff to get my mother into ICU.

The pulmonologist said: "She doesn't have pneumonia—her lungs are clear."

"But she's having trouble breathing—I heard a tiny percolating in her lungs yesterday."

After three hours a pulmonary technician arrived. My mother was finally moved to CCU after the technician confirmed she couldn't breathe. But they still ignored me. They still said she didn't have pneumonia.

Her temperature was now so low because of the ice that CCU was struggling to raise it.

A physician walked in with four-inch heels, tons of makeup and bottle blond hair:

"I think she has neuroleptic malignant syndrome."

"That's impossible. My mother isn't on any antipsychotics."

"You're a doctor?"

"I know what NMS is and she doesn't have it."

"Well the pulmonologist—Dr. Elude—thinks it's heat stroke."

"That's impossible too. She's been in a freezing house all summer."

"Well, pneumonia doesn't cause all these symptoms."

"Well—perhaps something is complicating it, but I know it's pneumonia. Are you going to save my mother doctor?"

"Yes," she said and walked away smiling.

The next day her fever had stabilized. She also had a tube down her nose. They were getting a ton of sludge out of her gut because she had an undiagnosed hiatal hernia, which was the source of her nausea.

I looked at the pint of darkened viscous fluid that had been in her tummy and then looked at her.

How could I have let that happen?

I couldn't figure out why they'd shut off the dredging and begin the feeding since it was the same tube in her left nostril and needed the same pathway. If all that sludge had to come up why were they putting more food down there? She had some weight on her, she wasn't going to starve.

I wanted that junk out. I watched that thick yellow mixture go down her nose and the black gunk come back up—seeing her exasperation that she was submitting to this.

Dr. Elude left a lengthy message on my phone that evening, that the second X-ray showed pneumonia. He didn't see it on the first X-ray because her lungs weren't fully inflated. He didn't admit that I had given him the diagnosis as soon as we met.

By Wednesday my mom was back in a regular room. I didn't like this. I asked Stephanie, the nurse in charge, to give her Elavil as it calmed her nerves.

"What's that? I never heard of it?"

"You've never heard of Elavil? Don't tell anyone; go home and study."

"I'm just being honest. I never heard of it."

"I'm being honest too, go home and study. I've never heard of anyone not hearing of Elavil. When did you graduate?"

"I just did," she said with a huge smile.

"Nancy, please get me something for the pain. I'm in great pain," my mom asked as soon as I entered her room. I asked one of the nurses to give her Oxycodone as her time was due.

"I'll do it in a few minutes, and I know she gets two."

"Isn't two a lot?" I asked, not wanting my mother to get nauseous.

"Dr. Elude said she could have two because she was in so much pain earlier."

We waited, but after two hours she still hadn't gotten one pill. "They still didn't do it? What's wrong with these people?" one of the nurses *not* assigned to my mother said when I begged for her help.

By Wednesday evening I knew my mother needed to be back in CCU. I lifted her sheets and saw her legs were blotchy and blue. Her face was changing. Both her right and left arm were holding the right bed bar as she looked not at me, but out the window.

She looked out the window for at least five minutes and I thought I saw something in her eyes.

Then she faced me: *"How can I do this?"* she asked. ●•●

52

....

116/20

Then it began.

She looked at me with a look I'd never seen and will never forget. *"I can't stay for you. I'm sorry Nancy—my daughter who I love so much. I don't want to leave you but I can't stay. I have to go. I don't know how to leave you—who will take care of you? I promised you, but I have to leave,"* her eyes said.

I stared back knowing.

A nurse in training looked on. She had given my mother a foot massage with cream earlier in the day. She had red hair. She came over and hugged me and pulled me out of the room. I didn't want to be pulled away from my mother. I didn't want her to come over. I didn't want her arms around me. It was the worst thing anyone could have done. I wanted my mother to stare at me for as long as she could tune in.

I began pleading with the staff: "PLEASE, PLEASE GET HER BACK TO CCU! PLEASE LOOK AT HER FACE. SHE'S PASTY, RED, SWEATING!"

Stephanie came in smiling: "I'm putting on the mask."

"Please don't put on the mask. Take her temperature. Please take her temperature right now!"

I ran out to get someone to take my mom's temperature and Stephanie was crying with a bunch of nurses around her.

"My mom is dying. Someone come, please help!"

I went back in the room and saw two aides had turned my mother upside down. My mother's arms were flailing in the air as she tried to catch her balance.

"What are you doing? Do you want to give her a stroke?" They smiled and left the room.

By the way they lifted her back up so fast—they knew they shouldn't have done that. I had already been through months of bed sheet maneuvering with my dad to know, no one did that with a critically ill patient.

An aide appeared with an ice pack. I grabbed it and put it on my mother's head. The aide left mumbling.

Now my mom's right arm and right leg began to shake and she began deliriously repeating with total desperation: ***"Get me the amitriptyline, get me the amitriptyline,"*** over and over nonstop. Her eyes were glued to mine as if she were literally drowning.

I called the hospital's main number from *within* the room: "Please, please—I need you to send someone to room 2010. My mother is dying and the staff is incompetent and doesn't realize she needs to be in CCU. Please hurry."

A different nurse came in: "I called CCU and they want her vitals."

By this time I was screaming: "TAKE HER TEMPERATURE BEFORE SHE DIES IN THIS ROOM AND YOU'LL ALL BE RESPONSIBLE!"

"I'm taking her blood pressure," she said—completely ignoring me.

Stephanie appeared: "I have witnesses."

Next a big woman came in: "I'm taking Stephanie's side."

"Great, so when my mother dies, I can tell them you said that."

Was this really happening? Was a boat capsized and the crew debating what to catch for dinner?

The energy shifted. Whoever this prejudiced woman was, she knew a lawsuit when she saw one and she knew I'd never forget her. She knew there was nothing she could do, to ever get on *my* side. She couldn't kiss my ass long enough for that to ever come true.

Within five minutes a male nurse entered, took my mother's rectal temperature—104.5—and scribbled it down on her chart. He quickly held up a gold pen: "You gave me this pen."

"What?"

"You don't remember me?"

"Who are you?"

"I took care of your mother when she was here for pneumonia the last time."

"You're the black belt who does magic tricks?"

"Yes."

"Gilbert?"

"Yes."

"Oh Gilbert, please help me, these people are crazy."

"Nancy, I'm getting her there. She was worse the last time. She'll make it."

Gilbert and I grabbed her bed and raced her down the hallway into an elevator while the nurses looked on. He stopped me before heading into CCU—for the first time I couldn't go in.

But before he closed the door: "Gilbert—tell me the top doctor for my mom!"

"Louis Saffran—Nancy, I promise to come see you as soon as she's stabilized."

I had given Gilbert a Sensa pen three years ago when she had pneumonia. It was a beautiful gold pen wrapped in gold leaf paper. I gave one to another nurse too who eventually traveled all the way to Brooklyn to become my patient. If Gilbert was around, maybe she'd live.

The enormous woman who said she's taking Stephanie's side, suddenly appeared: "They shouldn't have assigned Stephanie to your mom—she's a new nurse."

As if I'd ever think this woman was on my side—and not see me as a white woman. She realized too late that 'taking sides' may have cost my mom her life.

I went down to administration and asked them to switch her primary.

"Well, you have to get permission from her current primary first," she said.

I knew that wouldn't fly.

"I already got permission from the new doctor who said he'd take the case."

This was true. I immediately called Dr. Saffran, who called me back at midnight and said he'd take over. Things were looking up. I even got to speak with him again at 1:00 a.m. to fill him in. I couldn't ever get the other pulmonologist on the phone.

That night I got a call from the hospital at 3:00 a.m. asking if my mom could be intubated because she was no longer breathing that well on her own.

"Okay, but no trach." I knew my mom wouldn't want the trach.

I called Gilbert who called me back around 6:00 a.m.

"Don't worry Nancy, your mom was intubated last time too and she came out okay—she is breathing on her own, it's just to make sure."

When I went to visit my mom after she was intubated... I wasn't prepared.

Her neck—that tube. Duck—*foie gras*.

I wasn't prepared the intubation would look like that—a huge tube shoved down her throat with tape over it. Her neck was arched in a way that is perilous for people with MS. I also wasn't prepared she'd be that sedated, so sedated that she was unconscious.

She was in *that* room.

I wasn't sure if I was imagining it, but I thought this was the room that people died in. Or at least I thought she would die in that room and she wouldn't die if she were in a different room. I had this funny feeling they put the sickest people in there.

I sang *Bridge Over Troubled Water* and *You and Me Against the World*. I stroked her arm in between all the wires and large tubes everywhere. I asked the nurse about her heart because it was beating out of her chest—I could see it.

"Well, the cardiologist took her off the Verapamil."

"Why?"

"So she could fight the fever."

I understood the concept and I'm not a cardiologist but if a person was on Verapamil for over 16 years wasn't it better if their pulse was under 100 so their body could fight that fever instead of having a heart attack? Did you need to kill the person to rid them of their fever?

Within a split second of her explanation her BP went to 116/20.

I asked the nurse: "Her diastole is 20, how can that be?"

"Oh, it's okay as long as the systole is 116," blowing me off again.

This is how my mother's going to die, I instantly thought.

Normally I'd call the cardiologist who did this, but with my mother's neck like that and the fever still raging, another part of my brain entered. She didn't want this. Something was telling me to give up and let her be with my dad.

I walked out of her room at 5:00 p.m. to call Perlstein: "Her BP is 116/20. How can it be 20?"

"It's okay as long as the systole is 116," he said.

Even though Perlstein said it, I knew it couldn't be right. I thought maybe he didn't hear the 20.

"You know Nan, maybe this is what Mother wants — maybe she wants to be with Dad."

I called Gilbert. He said the 20 was okay too. He also said she was able to breath on her own even though they still had her hooked up. Somehow he was getting updates.

Darlene arrived after getting lost for three hours from Harlem. I went back into my mom's room, with my eyes on the monitor: Pulse 122.

I started to sing *Bridge Over Troubled Water,* and touched her arm.

Something flashed — ZERO.

The 122 mysteriously went to zero as soon as I touched her arm.

"What happened?" Darlene asked.

"She just died," I calmly said, just reporting the events.

A smiling nurse shot in: "She's coding — please leave."

"What? What is happening?" Darlene said again, alarmed.

We walked out and in a few seconds I *felt* her around me.

"She's gone."

A team ran into the room. I heard the smiling nurse greet them happily.

Then a well-coiffed female, arms folded, entered the room after scanning my face in the hallway. A man handed me a glass of cold water and brought a chair but I couldn't sit—I had to be ready to run to my mom if she came back to life.

The perfectly dressed woman came out with a 'been there, done that' look and spoke without me asking: "They're doing everything possible to help your mom."

"Tell me straight, she died, right." It was not a question.

"Yes, but they're trying to get a beat."

Phonies were apparent a mile away and this woman wasn't one of them. The smiling nurse came toward me. "Get her away from me," I said turning my face.

Then a young sweaty red-faced doctor came out of the room looking at the woman he'd have to give the bad news to.

"Her pupils?" I asked.

"You know?" a wave of relief over his face.

I cut him off: "Fixed and dilated?"

He gave me a questioning look.

"I'm an optometrist."

He didn't have to do the aching thing. What he didn't know was nothing he said was real anyway. I was some other person. It wasn't me. It wasn't *my* mother. Just a scene from someone else's life. Someone who was composed, who knew how to act.

Just the fact they were so incompetent made me stronger. It was a false strength. At least I knew it was fake—temporary. I knew the sledgehammer would hit unexpectedly, inconveniently. I wondered if I could handle it then. Long after the fact.

I knew how my mom would handle it. Quiet. Stoic without meaning to be stoic. She'd hear it and leave—zero drama. Attention was never her thing. Still—they kept offering me to sit. I wasn't going to faint.

"Stop the CPR," I said.

They went to tell them to stop.

"Wait"—*Should I let her go?*

"No. Stop it. I want to stop."

Just then: "They got a pulse."

I decided without deciding—thoughts of her being intubated, of her knowing, of me knowing she'd kill me if I let them continue—many conversations flashed in an instant.

What kind of beat? What did it matter? Her pupils were fixed and dilated.

"Would you please give her some morphine? I know it doesn't matter, but would you please?"

"She doesn't need it," a chorus of assholes replied.

How did they know what she needed? And who cared if she got some? They still had to remove the breathing tube and what if it hurt? She still had a beat.

The well-coiffed woman said: "I lost my parents."

"When do you get over it?"

"You don't," wiping a tear from her eye.

Then someone asked if I wanted to say goodbye to her. I knew she already said goodbye to me. I felt her.

But when I went in, her face began to turn white. It wasn't like my dad—his face turned white while he was still alive, his skin stretched over his bones, still talking.

But even though my mom's face wasn't emaciated like my dad's, she still had her same face.

It was my world that was turning white. As the white started coming in and the red receded in a perfect fade-out, I turned not to see. I needed to remember her still alive.

Out by the car I called again and begged for them to give her the morphine.

They were supposed to call as soon as they lost the beat. They never called and by morning I put all thoughts out of my mind of what could have happened overnight—how she may have lingered with that lone beat. I didn't even look at the time of (that word) on the (that word) certificate. I didn't want to think she was all alone, all ghost white and wherever they might have put her.

I can't remember when I called Lewis but I still needed to know about the 20. Finally I got my answer.

"That's not acceptable to me—the systolic pressure is okay, but you need more diastolic pressure to perfuse the coronary artery, so we would shoot for 40-50 minimum for diastole," Lewis said.

He also concurred discontinuing the Verapamil was the wrong move.

When I spoke with my own cardiologist months later, he said: "So they killed her."

Perlstein called later: "Nan, forgive me. I don't think I heard correctly. It can't be 20. Listen, this is the equation: [(2 x diastolic) + systolic] /3 —you must have a minimum of 60. But your mom was 52…can't be."

My father passed on Friday July 8th; it was Friday July 15th.

I could say my mom passed and sometimes I can use another word, like 'die,' but only in some tenses. I could only say my father passed. I could not use that other word for him. I have no idea why.

Lewis said pneumonia is how chronically ill people go—that it's the gentleman's way toward death or something like that.

If we were at Columbia Hospital, she'd be here. But not the way she would have wanted. Not without her Lenny.

She had been breaking down all that time I thought he was the sicker one. She was dying right alongside him. Holding on for him. And when I got home from Westchester, and she knew where her Lenny was—her body finally stopped working.

We had to wait for Sunday again. Darlene stayed over that night. I picked some of my own clothes for my mom to wear: a beautiful white skirt and white cotton knit top with a sweater.

I put a pair of my dad's eyeglasses, along with a Queen from a deck of cards, into a velvet eyewear satchel.

Then I began looking through some of her papers. I don't know why I happened to go to that particular corner of the house. But what I found startled me.

I found a huge amount of Deanna's hair that Dreck had sent with a letter telling my mother that she can't come see Deanna.

There was another letter my mother wrote begging to visit her. It was never mailed.

And there was yet another letter my mom wrote telling off someone who had betrayed me... *Thanks Mom!*

Then I saw all of her notes — they were endless.

One note was from Dreck's first visit with my folks. My mother had to defend why my father didn't have more money socked away. I remember that day. The sinister way Dreck was leaning over the kitchen table peering at my dad and haranguing him about money. This was an extremely unusual dynamic because my parents never spoke about money. Part of it had to do with Deanna not having enough for what Dreck would consider a dowry, as I realized when Deanna piped up:

"See? I have some money in my family."

This greatly upset my mom. My father was more prescient — worried all of Dreck's money was tied up in real estate.

I now remembered the two dreams I had after Dreck's visit:

An enormous bear was on top of a log cabin. Deanna and I were inside. The bear swooped down and ran off with Deanna.

The other dream was of a skunk near the cabin.

There were too many notes of anguish after Dreck took Deanna away: "He won't let me speak to my own daughter, he won't let me see her." And a second letter she never sent: "Please let me speak with my daughter. Is she okay? Maybe if I'm up to it I can visit her... I'd only

301

stay five minutes..."

There was also a letter from Dreck sent long after the move describing Deanna's condition: "There's really nothing that can be done. The tumor has grown too large and she'd be a vegetable with surgery. Deanna sits with the remote but doesn't speak. She sits in the dark. I force her to shower every two weeks but she fights me because it burns."

There was zero admission that when the tumor was small—when she had the chance not to be a vegetable—that he prevented it. There was no mention that the burning sensation was from the Lamictal he still gave her.

Did he enjoy writing this to my mother?

Guilt was rising over me like a tidal wave of poison, until I turned one note over to read: "Nancy—Thank God I had you." I clutched it to my chest like an antidote.

Then I found another gem—an entire journal she kept of my first 24 months...*how come I'd never seen this?* There were two other journals of my sisters until they turned six. I stashed them back in the corner for a time I could pour over them.

Before I did I couldn't help but read the first few pages:

"I thought Duffy was the best thing in our family, until Nancy came along," said Leslie. When my mom told Deanna she talked too much: "Well—what are you there for—just to look at?" Deanna responded at four years old.

When I was two years old, my mother was taking me for a walk when a strange child grabbed my teddy bear out of my arms. I grabbed it back. The other child started crying. I handed my teddy to the child with tears in my eyes. *How will I ever know if my tears were because I felt bad for that idiot kid or because I gave up my teddy?*

I put a lock of Deanna's hair into the satchel.

The funeral home was getting my mom at the hospital Sunday. I asked the Rabbi how to bring her clothes there in time. I quickly learned what I didn't want to know.

"You don't need to Nancy."

"Oh no, don't tell me. The shroud. *Oh no.*"

"Nancy, it's not a religious thing. It's so no one appears to have more or less than another when we return to God … it's so everyone is equal."

"Then what happened to my dad's bathrobe? They just laid it alongside him?"

"Yes."

"Oh no."

"Nancy, it's not a big deal."

"So what about the other stuff? Can you put in this velvet satchel and pictures?"

"Yes, we can do that Sunday."

"Okay. But I don't want to see. I don't want you to do it in front of me."

"Don't worry, I'll do it."

Again, Singh, Morda and now Darlene drove up to Westchester on Sunday. I wore the same exact outfit.

I crouched down to sit on the grass but noticed a worm and immediately stood up. I couldn't take my eyes off of this worm. For some reason I pictured this place worm-free. The worm was wiggling its way toward 'The Inside.' (I still can't say what the inside is.) The worm kept moving closer and closer as I hoped it would go a different way.

I grabbed the Rabbi's arm, interrupting his speech and whispered: "There's a worm, please get it away."

He whispered back: *"Where is it?"*

"There," I quietly cried.

He took his enormous foot and moved a ton of dirt out of the way until the worm was clear out of sight. But then I couldn't stop looking for other worms, or wondering if they were all around them down there.

The Rabbi continued his speech: "Nancy, your mother couldn't live without your father."

He stopped and thought about it and smiled and repeated it as if it wasn't a speech anymore:

"Your mother just couldn't live without your father."

Then I asked the Rabbi to repeat what we did with my father. Asking the spirits to let my mom hang around me until I could join them. Not to leave. To stay close by.

The Rabbi got his book and said: "Nancy, there's something in here that says exactly what you're saying."

But before we could begin, the diggers came by. They wanted to go home.

"Por favor, cinco minutos. Es mi madre—por favor," I pleaded.

The Latin men had manners and instantly moved away, looking confused and also respectful. But the white guys kept hovering and continued to hurry me.

Another Rabbi was hovering too. He was an older Rabbi—looking lost. He kept crushing a white paper bag, like a senile old bag lady.

Did he want to make it worse?

"Why is that Rabbi crinkling that bag? Please tell him to stop," I asked my Rabbi.

Finally finished, the Rabbi pulled me aside: "Nancy, you're supposed to tip that Rabbi. He schleps all the way up here. That bag has candles for your parents. He stayed with your mom. You don't have to, but most people do."

I know he didn't stay with my mom Friday night, which still pained me. I was paying so much money to do the traditional thing and not leave my mom alone. Yet she was alone in some slab room, because this was an Orthodox place the Rabbi hooked me up with and they wouldn't go there until after Saturday sundown.

"I didn't know Rabbi. How much?" I asked, feeling both surprise and disgust. I handed him $200. "I don't have more."

"That's more than generous."

As soon as I got back in the car, before I got my seatbelt on, the car started backing up!

For some idiotic reason, Singh decided to back up to the entrance half a mile away at 50 mph instead of going the few feet forward toward the exit. I became more than ill—something took over.

"What are you doing?" I screamed.

Was he trying to time travel? Did he want me to bury my mother again? Was he going to back up all the way before she got sick? Rolling back the movie I was in?

I couldn't help but remember. *The sledgehammer hit.*

Her last look at me right before the final delirium—I could see it as clearly as if it were happening again.

Did my dad call her from the window she was looking through? Was she wishing she could pull herself up with both of her hands gripping that bar, but unable to with all the wires attached? Or was she thinking of how she was going to tell me she's leaving?

"How can I do this?"

I still see her turning toward me slowly with that look she'd never had before.

The last moments we have with someone—we don't often know they're the last. If we knew, wouldn't we collect a whole bunch more way before? I couldn't ask her for more though. I'd had a lifetime of them.

In my greatest pain I was always cognizant of how lucky I was.

I didn't have to waste therapy sessions on abusive parents like so many who were told they weren't good enough. My therapy was devoted mostly to bad guys.

And without my father— *Who's gonna tell me I'm gorgeous in my glasses and no makeup? Who's gonna tell me "he's a jerk," when some guy hurts me again?*

I had no distance to losing my parents, the way you automatically do when you have your own family to lean on.

Bram was right: *"You're going to need someone."*

I had no children to smile at me or to hug or worry about and protect. I only had my cats. The last three. They would now have all my love. And soon I'd lose them too.

Bisqui was diagnosed with adenocarcinoma a week after my mom's passing. It was located in the sinus cavities and impossible to fully excise. After multiple visits to have his sinuses drained, requiring him to be knocked out and fitted with a breathing tube—I took him to an extravagant place where they opened him up, took out all the gunk, and finally diagnosed it as cancer.

When he was a kitten, I carried him in my lab coat breast pocket during eye exams. He was so tiny only his head and one paw would peek out of the pocket. This gave him the marsupial need to always be under covers.

When I slept over at the office I'd awake to see his orange head on the pillow next to mine, with his body elongated under the blanket as if he thought himself human. Sometimes I'd nearly sit on him not realizing he was that little lump under the quilt.

These cats were all born in my office after I found their mother under my car eating garbage. They moved in with my mom at five weeks and stayed five years, until Leslie forced them back to the office.

Now 14 years later, the cat I was closest to was walking around the house sounding like a Slurpee and refusing to let me drain him. The only other option was 10 days of radiation and some chemo. I knew Bisqui would say: "Don't do that to me. Just leave me be. Don't make me stay in a prison with strangers."

I don't know how I'll come home to the sound of no one else breathing. This is a worry.

I was in a store tonight buying a shower curtain when a stylish yet extremely obese customer said: "Smile" to the cashier. The sad cashier was a thin, tired Indian woman who didn't mask it with food.

"What an idiot to say 'smile.' How does she know how you feel?" I said.

The Indian woman then gave me the warmest smile, while the owner chimed in: "She wasn't smiling, and all she's doing is eating for her pain."

The pressure to smile can be daunting—even if you're happy.

A truly happy person doesn't rely on external displays of contentment.

It's the unhappy people that need you to 'smile.'

Even in dire circumstances—happiness can remain. It can be found in love, care, comfort—things that are given and received. Things you might never know were there if you weren't the one feeling them. But they are there.

True contentment shows itself in unexpected ways.

I remembered the afternoon my mother showed me this truth—one I suppose I had always known intuitively but never clearly defined.

I had spent the afternoon cleaning my parents' room. I was changing the sheets after my father had wet the bed, when my mom said: "You threw out all my creatures."

"What are you talking about?"

"Those are my creatures…" she said, motioning to the wastebasket of balled up tissue.

"Ma, you mean those tissues weren't used?"

"No, I picture them as animals."

I thought about the tissue I had thrown away. I realized that what I had assumed was haphazard crumpling could have easily been intentional folds made by hobbled hands.

"Mom, wait a minute, all these years you never told me about this."

"I make them into animals. I was afraid to tell you. I thought you'd think I'm silly."

"*You do?* Like what kinds of animals?"

"Well, that one over there was a duck. The one next to him was a giraffe—but you threw him out."

"Mom, I love you so much. I think that's the coolest thing."

In all her pain—her bent, aching body, her breaking heart—my mother was still creating—she was amusing herself in quiet, secret ways. In spite of everything, she was content. She was teaching me. Little tiny things I was taking with me now, wishing crumpled up tissues made me smile too.

The truth is I wouldn't want to be anyone else. I've tried to imagine someone whose skin I'd want to be in. Maybe for a day—someone I admired. I couldn't think of too many.

Maybe having Shirley Bassey's vocals for a day, or feeling the thrill of an Olympian skier's jump in midair, or being in Zoë Wanamaker's coat in *Electra*—but not even for a day, maybe an hour.

Even if I can't stop crying I wouldn't want to trade who I am for someone else. Even if I get down on myself, something inside won't give me up.

So, I'm making creatures. I'm doing what Sandra would do.

In spite of circumstance—illness, pain, betrayal—and in spite of the quiet I fear, I will continue to love, care, and comfort—to give and receive. To create.

I won't need another person to 'smile' to tell me what I already know.

And when I fill my home with sounds again—when I meet that stand-up man who smells, sounds, and feels right to me—maybe it'll be half of what my parents had…

Half would be tremendous. 👓

ACKNOWLEDGMENTS

Nils Parker gave me what I couldn't find in any editor until him—trust and competence. He believed in my story and guided me through this odyssey as a first-time author. His confidence inspired me when he encouraged me to record an audio version.

Nils sent me to Kevin Fecu at John Marshall Media for the audio production. Kevin gave me the space and flexibility I needed for this personal story. Yet if not for Eric West to engineer the project—I wouldn't have felt comfortable enough to do it.

Eric West mastered countless hours to create an authentic read—always ready with those mini chocolate bars to sustain me. Fun was the last thing I expected but that's what I had with each session, along with the tears.

Robert Lascaro rescued me when things got tough—there is no one with more selflessness and empathy than Bob. He involved me in every step of the interior layout and book design. And before I realized, became a close friend.

Joe Frazz—who has a heart to soothe both animals and humans when he's behind and beside the lens.

Charles Salzberg—my go-to for advice and rectitude—because he has that one elusive thing: Integrity.

I owe special gratitude to:

Dr. Abraham Perlstein—who passed away several months after my parents. He did read the manuscript though and smiled as he overcame his humility to tell me he wasn't only our hero, but was receiving a 'HERO' award in Portland, for helping countless patients swim upstream. He gave us 13 extra years we would have lost without him. I still try to picture him 'sitting on my shoulder.'

Dr. Lewis Mehl-Madrona — who recorded from a studio in Maine during a break from his nonstop schedule. I don't have to thank Lewis for saving my life — because he already knows.

Jimmy Halperin — who not only reads — he stands in for my family with his sax to complete it.

All my readers have a permanent place in my heart:

Dr. Leslie St. Louis said: "It would be an honor," when I asked him to read for my father. I needed a base baritone and someone who has the masculinity for this role. Leslie somehow tapped into the most painful storylines—and endured as many takes as needed to make it genuine.

Arthur Russell — for years I've called Arthur my 'lawyer shrink,' so it was fitting he play Dr. Perlstein — but I didn't know his talent as a litigator also extended to the role of Rabbi.

Nathan Yelen — only Nathan could play the many facets of Bram as true and natural. The audio never would have happened without Nathan's sensitivity and insight.

Dr. Myron Schwartz — did more than save my liver when he said: "Well — I don't know why I wouldn't," when I asked him to read.

My professor, mentor, and friend Dr. Jerome Sherman who saved too many of my patients with the correct diagnosis when the ophthalmologists I referred to failed in their role. I don't know how to ever thank Jerry for his years of friendship.

Dr. Howard Fried has taught me I have a friend I didn't know existed. We mustered through 4 years of graduate school together with hardly a word but wound up working 3 minutes away from each other. Howie has remained a source of camaraderie in a career where I've often felt like Rodney Dangerfield: *"I don't get no respect."*

Dr. Paul Patsalis — saved me from storing over 15,000 records in my garage — when we decided in 5 minutes on a handshake — after a 5-year search — that I could entrust my patients to him.

Many of my readers sat in 3 hours of traffic on the L.I.E. after working all day, to help tell my story: Steven Dimitriou, Tommy Doyle, Thomas Fetherston, Pino Fiduli, Johannes Lagerweij, Stuart Sherman, Paldeep Singh, Mark Spielman, and my navigator Eric West.

And for their unwavering support:

My cousin Michelle — who always tells me I can do anything
My cousin Sharon — who knew when I needed family
My cousin Chris — who's given me a lifeline
Johanna — who somehow has become family
Susanne — the only person who reminds me of me
Cisco — takes my side as if it's the only side
Darlene — was there at the lowest point
Susan — when I need someone to admire
David and Gary — forever protecting me
Trevor — still smiling when you say *Sandra*
Jose — for making her days more beautiful

For all my nonhuman creatures:

You've kept me going when no one else was around. Someday those silly humans will learn your language but they still don't understand their own.

ABOUT THE AUTHOR

Nancy Glassman owned the oldest Optometric Practice in New York State.

She has shared this raw story so you aren't blind to the 'experts' who are.

If you want to save the life of a loved one, or simply yearn to lessen their suffering—you won't miss the signs—you'll know what to do.

Who knows—the life you save— may be your own.

Made in United States
North Haven, CT
14 August 2023

40302461R00198